Artist of the Reformation

The Story of Albrecht Dürer

by Joyce McPherson
With Illustrations by Albrecht Dürer

*To my children—May you always see the
beauty in God's creation*

www.greenleafpress.com
1570 Old Laguardo Rd
Lebanon, TN 37087

Table of Contents

Albrecht's father, Self Portrait

Chapter 1

"Love and delight are better teachers than compulsion."
Albrecht Dürer

A Golden Bird

R ain spattered on the thick studio windows, and by the fire a large gray dog snoozed in the warmth. Nearby, a boy sat beside his father on a weathered oak bench. The boy's yellow hair was a contrast to the man's gray hair, but their eyes were the same: large and watching.

"Albrecht, hand me the burin," his father said quietly.

Though he was eight years old, not even apprentice age, the boy handled the tool with care.

"Father, will you make the bird, now?"

"First I will sketch the proportions. Remember, if you lack a true foundation, it is impossible for you to make anything right and well."

Albrecht watched as his father lightly outlined the figure of a bird. Then, with delicate strokes, he engraved the proud neck, the clenched talons, and every feather on the wings. Albrecht barely breathed as he watched his father work. In the candlelight, the boy's well-defined cheekbones and high-bridged nose seemed as finely etched as the golden bird.

The wind changed direction and the fire hissed as rain was driven down the chimney. Neither Albrecht nor his father noticed.

Young Albrecht, Self Portrait, 1484

Albrecht's father carefully laid the golden bowl on the table. "I learned to make this design from my father. He was Anton Dürer, and he was the goldsmith in the village of Gyula in the kingdom of Hungary."

Albrecht loved to hear his father's stories. He waited for his father to continue.

"His family raised horses and cattle in the nearby town of Eytas, but my father wanted to do something different. His father saw that he was clever with his hands, so he apprenticed him to a goldsmith. My father loved to make things with his hands and he taught me his trade."

"And then you came to Nurnberg and married mother," Albrecht added.

His father laughed. "God brought me to Nurnberg to work for a fine goldsmith. I never guessed I would one day marry his daughter."

He held the bowl in the candlelight to inspect his work. Albrecht gasped in surprise at the beautiful figure his father had engraved. The light glinted on the intricate figure so that the golden bird looked almost alive.

"Now I have shown you something," his father said. "Do you have something to show me?"

Albrecht reached deep into his pocket and brought out a small object for his father. "I found this today." On his palm lay a small brown nut in its shell.

"It is quaintly shaped," remarked his father.

Albrecht rolled the shell in his hand. "I have never seen another one like it. I will show it to Willibald when he returns tomorrow."

Albrecht's father took the nut in his own hand. "When I see something like this it reminds me that it is God who creates all these wondrous things."

Albrecht heard the door turning gently on its hinges. He looked up to see his mother standing in the doorway. She shook her head in mock surprise. "I wondered where the two of you would be on such a rainy evening. The apprentices are finished and you are still in the workshop!"

"See what we made," said Albrecht eagerly.

His mother took the bowl in her hands and gently touched the bird with a long, thin finger. Before her marriage she had been trained as a goldsmith, and she still understood the craft. "This is the finest work in the city of Nurnberg," she declared. "Only one man could have made this."

She carefully placed the bowl on the shelf, then bustled about the fire, making it safe for the night. "There will be time enough for work when Albrecht is an apprentice," she said cheerfully. "Now it is time for dinner."

When Albrecht and his father arrived, the rest of the family was already seated. Albrecht's parents sat at each end of the long table. Albrecht shared a bench with his brothers, Sebald and Heironymous. Anthoni and Ursula shared the opposite bench, and baby Hans slept nearby in his cradle. Albrecht as the oldest was expected to serve his little brothers and sister.

Albrecht's father began the meal with a prayer. Then he ladled the rich stew while Albrecht passed the plates. "Your mother has made an excellent meal," he commented. Albrecht heard his father speak of his mother's virtues so often, that he was convinced that his mother was the most talented and excellent woman in all the realm. He would have been surprised to learn that there were other mothers who could make a delicious stew or raise children as well as his own mother.

That night Albrecht lay in bed as his mother prayed for him and his brothers. Through parted lashes he could just see her hands, the long fingers lightly touching. His mother finished her prayer and gently kissed each of her sons.

Albrecht savored the pleasant warmth of the blankets. His stomach felt full of good food, but best of all was the thought that tomorrow he would see Willibald.

Willibald was Albrecht's best friend. From before the boys were born, Albrecht's family had rented the small house that lay behind the larger home of Willibald's family. Only a small courtyard separated them, and they had played countless hours there. Already Albrecht had ideas for new games they could play tomorrow.

The new day dawned clear and bright. Albrecht hurried through his chores. He had barely finished his sweeping, when Willibald knocked on the door. The boys spent a satifying morning exchanging news of the past few months and inventing new games.

As they played, the dog, Hund, frisked around Albrecht's legs and almost knocked him over. Albrecht patted a place by the garden wall and coaxed his dog. "Come here, boy. Come here."

"I don't think this game is going to work," said Willibald. Though he was the same age as Albrecht, he was short and round while Albrecht was tall and thin. Willibald took a tentative step toward the excited dog.

Hund's wagging tail thumped Willibald on the back and he retreated to the far end of the yard.

Albrecht leaned against Hund, and pushed him toward the desired spot. "I'm sure it will work if we can get Hund to sit down," he said through clenched teeth.

Suddenly Hund sat, and Albrecht fell on top of him.

"It's your father coming," said Willibald. "He must have heard him."

From the alley behind his house, Albrecht heard the steady tread of his father's boots on the cobbled street. Hund pricked his ears and sat at attention.

"Quick, before he moves!" said Albrecht. "You have to be Hercules and escape past the dog Cerberus."

Willibald sprang into action and ran past the now-quiet dog as closely as he dared. "My house is the overworld," he cried. He ran the short distance between Albrecht's house and his own. He was almost to his door when he stopped. "Wait, the story doesn't go this way. Don't you remember how Hercules took Cerberus with him?"

Albrecht looked doubtfully from his dog to his friend. "How did he do that?"

"I think Orpheus lulled him to sleep..."

Just then the gate creaked on its hinges and Albrecht's father entered. Hund quivered with excitement but remained steadfastly in place while his master greeted the two boys.

"We are playing Hercules," explained Albrecht.

His father raised his eyebrows in question.

"It's a Greek story that Willibald's father told to him. Hercules was the strongest man who ever lived. He was the only one who could ever pass by the fierce dog, Cerberus. Hund is Cerberus."

Hund barked and Albrecht's father patted him affectionately. "I wonder if Hercules is hungry after his adventures. I think I smell ginger cakes."

Albrecht and Willibald sniffed the air as hungrily as the mythical Cerberus, then with Hund at their heels they raced across the small yard to Albrecht's door.

Albrecht's mother served the boys generous slices of ginger cake. "Willibald, you will have to visit us when we move to our new home," she said.

The boys looked at each other in dismay. Willibald's family had just returned from months of travel. Would the boys have to be parted again?

"Don't look so sad," said Albrecht's father. "Our new house is a few short blocks away. You boys will be school-age and old enough to walk to see each other."

Hund poked his nose around the door, and Albrecht fed him some crumbs. "I guess we can still see each other," said Albrecht.

"But it will be a lot farther to run to the overworld," said Willibald. The boys laughed at their private joke.

Study of a Dog, 1520

Chapter 2

"Let none be ashamed to learn, for a good work requireth good counsel."

Albrecht Dürer

School

The massive walls and frowning rocks of the Nurnberg Citadel loomed over Albrecht as he ran to school. His new home stood in the road called *Unter der Vesten* which meant that the street ran below the Citadel or *Veste*. In the two years since they had moved there, the Dürer family had found many good friends in the neighborhood. Each of the homes lay above successful shops, which tantalized Albrecht with their interesting machines and activities.

Albrecht peered through the open door of his godfather's printing room as he passed. He listened for the thud of the presses and smelled the fresh ink. Further on his school route he passed the painting and print design workshop of his father's friend, Michael Wolgemut. He was disappointed to see the doors of the studio were closed.

The sun rose as he turned the corner to the Market Place. The two thin towers of the Cathedral of St. Sebald cast long shadows in his path. The church was named for the patron saint of Nurnberg. Albrecht let his mind roam to stories of the famous hermit who preached the gospel in this region over 400 years ago. Many colorful stories were told about the saint, but the one that drew Albrecht's imagination was the story of the lad who mocked

Saint Sebald

the honorable saint and was swallowed up by the earth as a result.

Albrecht renewed his pace, and crossed the Meat Bridge. He arrived breathless at the Church of St. Lawrence as the bells of the church tolled over the awakening city. In the next few minutes shops would open, tradesmen would begin their work, and the steady traffic of Nurnberg's city would pass through the Market Place. Albrecht sighed. There were so many rich things to see, but he could not stop to see them today.

Albrecht pushed open the heavy door and took his place on the bench with the other students. His schoolmaster cast a disapproving look in his direction. Albrecht bowed his head and tried to listen to the priest as he intoned the service in Latin.

After the church service the boys filed out of the church. Albrecht's thoughts had grown quiet during the service. The grand arches and domed ceiling of the church filled him with a sense of awe. There was something sacred and holy there. With a backward glance, Albrecht caught sight of the stone carvings around the church door.

Above the door was illustrated the crucifixion. The carving was as intricate as his father's gold work. Albrecht thought Jesus on the cross looked noble and sad. He wondered how the sculptor was able to show the Christ so clearly in stone.

Albrecht's schoolmaster tapped him on the shoulder. "Enough dreaming for today," he said sternly. Obediently, Albrecht followed the other students to the school room.

In Albrecht's school the boys sat by two's on narrow benches. The schoolmaster led the boys in chanting conjugations of Latin verbs. As Albrecht chanted, "*Porto, portas, portat, portamus, portatis, portant*," he tried his best to concentrate on his lessons. His father told him that everything he learned would help him one day. He had shown Albrecht an engraving he had made in Latin. Albrecht smiled as he thought of engraving "*Porto, portas, portat...*" on a large silver urn.

The schoolmaster tacked a large map to the wall. "Today we will learn about Nurnberg," he began. "The city of Nurnberg is a free imperial city. We do not pay taxes to bishops or dukes as other cities do. Instead we pay our taxes directly to the Emperor of the Holy Roman Empire."

He paused to ascertain that the boys were suitably impressed. "This is the map of the Holy Roman Empire, and here is Nurnberg. The city is at the crossroads of overland routes. Does anyone remember what is imported from Venice?"

Conrad, a large-boned boy with a shock of red hair, raised his hand and the schoolmaster acknowledged him.

"Spices, silks and jewels."

"Correct. Here is Hungary. What comes from Hungary?"

Albrecht raised his hand at once. He remembered his father's stories of his homeland. The teacher acknowledged him and he stood to answer. "Horses, copper, silver, and gold are imported from Hungary."

The teacher nodded his approval, then went on to explain that amber, fish and furs came from the Baltic, and woolen cloth from the Netherlands. "You can see why Nurnberg has become a prosperous city. In fact, Nurnberg has agreements for toll-free trade with seventy cities in the realm."

After morning lessons the boys had a lunch break. They quickly devoured their simple meals of crusty bread and peppery Nurnberg sausage so that they might use their time to play. Sometimes they played with a leather ball made by Philip's father, who was a tanner. In the spring when the Pegnitz River flowed faster, they liked to hang over the Meat Bridge and throw sticks into the river. However, this afternoon the boys had a new idea.

"Let's see if we can corner Hildebrand," said the red-haired Conrad. He was the son of a blacksmith and respected among the other boys for his large size and strength.

"I know where she goes to the Pegnitz River to drink," offered Philip.

Albrecht noticed some of the younger boys had turned pale at the thought of Hildebrand. She was the largest pig in the neighborhood, and the meanest one, too. In Nurnberg pigs were allowed to forage freely in the streets. Some of them, like Hildebrand, became almost wild. "I don't know..." Albrecht began.

"Come on, you don't have to be afraid of a little mud," jeered Conrad. "Doesn't your mother send you to the public baths on Saturday?"

Albrecht shut his mouth hard so that he would not pick a fight with Conrad. He was almost as fearsome as Hildebrand. "I was going to say that we will need teams, and there must be enough of the bigger boys on each team, or someone might get trampled."

Conrad considered this for a moment. He swelled with importance, since he was clearly the largest boy. "Philip and I will be captains," he declared. "We will each take three boys from the first level and four boys from the second level. That leaves one extra person." He stood over Albrecht and grinned. "Albrecht will be the extra person who drives out Hildebrand."

Albrecht was about to protest, but the relief on the faces of the other boys told him that no one else would be volunteering for the job. He looked down the alley that ran behind the school. "If I can scare her into running down this alley, your two teams will have to do the rest."

The boys scattered to their stations, and Albrecht turned his face toward the river and Hildebrand's favorite drinking spot.

It did not take long for him to find her. Her huge bulk lay right in his path. With a yell that frightened Albrecht almost as much as the pig, he charged her. The last thing he remembered were the tiny points of red fire in Hildebrand's eyes.

When Albrecht opened his eyes, Conrad was leaning over him. His face was so white that his freckles looked more like the pox. "We thought you were dead," he said in a hushed voice.

"What happened?" asked Albrecht. He felt too swirly to sit up.

"You chased her right into our trap, but she broke out the church gate."

"I've never seen such a fury as got into that pig," added Philip as way of a compliment.

Albrecht slowly rose to his feet amidst cheers and a hearty slap on the back from Philip. He was almost a hero.

Though Albrecht enjoyed the comraderie of his classmates, his favorite part of school was geometry.

One warm afternoon flies buzzed around the open school window. Some of the boys slumped on their benches, but Albrecht was listening intently.

"If you will pursue a trade, you must learn the elements of geometry," said the schoolmaster as he drew a circle on a board. "To make a proper circle, you must construct a figure that is the same distance at every point from the center." He jabbed the center of the circle with the charcoal for emphasis. "The ancients taught us the use of the compass and rule. We will learn how to use these and several useful ideas."

Albrecht watched with growing wonder as his teacher began with simple lines and showed how to accurately divide them, draw perpendicular lines, isosceles triangles, and perfect circles.

That evening Albrecht eagerly reported all that he had learned to his father. His father smiled and continued working while his son spoke.

"Father, what do you think of this idea to make a perfect circle?" Albrecht asked.

"It is a good rule for a good symbol."

"What do you mean by a symbol?" asked Albrecht.

His father paused from his work for a moment and reached for a scrap of paper. "In my trade we use symbols to stand for other things. For example, the cross is a symbol of the Christ, and a triangle is a symbol for the Trinity."

"How is the circle a symbol?" asked Albrecht.

"Ah, that is a joyful symbol. It is the symbol of everlasting salvation."

Albrecht looked confused, so his father took one of the volumes of the Bible from the shelf. "This was a gift from your godfather, Herr Koberger. These two books contain the entire Bible. Now that you can read Latin, you can understand the words. Listen carefully." His father opened the heavy tome and read from the book of Hebrews: "*et consummatus factus est omnibus obtemperantibus sibi causa salutis aeternae.*"

"Can you translate this?"

Slowly Albrecht began, "And...being made perfect...he is made to all...submitting to him...the cause...of salvation...eternal."

"Good! In other words, "And being made perfect, he became to all who submit to Him the cause or author of eternal salvation."

"I still do not understand."

Albrecht's father smoothed the page of the Bible and his eyes softened. "The Bible teaches us that our Savior, Jesus Christ, was perfect so that he could give eternal salvation to those who submit to him. Eternal salvation is one of the most joyful things man has ever known. That is why I say the circle is a joyful symbol."

While his father worked, Albrecht studied the figures his father had drawn. The circle had no beginning or end. As he traced the circle with his finger he thought about his father's words and the idea of eternal salvation.

Chapter 3

"She constantly gave us holy admonitions with deep earnestness and she always had great thought for our soul's health. I cannot enough praise her good works and the compassion she showed to all, as well as her high character. This my pious Mother bare and brought up eighteen children."

Albrecht Dürer

A New Baby

O ne morning Albrecht came downstairs to breakfast and found his mother in the middle of a circle of his brothers and sisters. She cradled a new baby in her arms! The tiny baby opened his eyes and fixed his brothers and sisters with a wide-eyed stare. While Albrecht and his four brothers hung back, his two sisters rushed to see the baby.

"Isn't he sweet!" said Ursula as she stroked one of the baby's tiny hands.

"Sweet," echoed Agnes, who was barely more than a baby herself.

Albrecht watched his mother who was smiling at the new baby. With her eyes downcast, she looked just like a painting of Mary with the baby Jesus. Albrecht imagined that the soft glow of the firelight was like a halo around the heads of the baby and his mother.

Heironymous tentatively stepped closer and leaned against his mother's knee. "Look what I brought for the baby." He held out a bunch of wild flowers, which had wilted in his tight grip. "Can the baby hold them?"

The Madonna in a Circle

"I think they would be beautiful next to his cradle, don't you think?" she replied.

Albrecht added Heironymous to his picture. He could be the young John the Baptist, come to see his cousin. The gift of flowers made the picture complete, except perhaps for a few more animals. Albrecht tried to imagine Hund in the picture. Too shaggy perhaps. A puppy of Hund would fit.

"Albrecht, you are so quiet today," said his mother. "Would you like to hold the baby?"

Albrecht rose awkwardly. "I don't know if I could. He is so little."

"If you can handle a delicate golden bowl, I think you can handle a baby." She placed the bundle in Albrecht's arms. The baby was very light and warm in his layers of blankets. He had fallen asleep, and he gave a tiny sigh as he settled into his big brother's arms.

Albrecht smiled in spite of himself.

"Another blessing from God," whispered his mother as he

returned his baby brother to her arms.

Albrecht's father took the family Bible from the shelf and opened to the second page. Albrecht watched as he wrote in careful script:

Item: in the year 1481 after Christ's birth, in the first hour of the day of St. Peter in Chains, my wife bore me my twelfth child, and Jobst Haller's man, Nicolas by name was the godfather, and he named my son Peter.

"Father, why do you say the baby is your twelfth child?" asked Albrecht. "There are only Sebald, Heironymous, Anthoni, Ursula, Hans, Agnes and me."

Albrecht's father grew somber and he drew his son to sit beside him on the bench. "Albrecht, before you were born we had a little daughter, Barbara, and a son, Hans. They died in a plague when you were very young. The year after the plague your mother had twin girls named Agnes and Margaretha who died soon after they were born. They are in heaven now, but they are our children just the same."

Albrecht was quiet for a few moments. "I remember Mother crying when Agnes and Margaretha died." He looked again at the tiny bundle in his Mother's arms. "God won't let this baby die, will He?"

"We will have to pray for protection for our new baby," replied his Father. "But the midwife says the baby looks strong and healthy."

Albrecht returned to his mother's side and gently touched the baby's smooth cheek.

Soon after the baby's birth, Albrecht's father was selected to be the street captain for their block of houses. The neighborhood had a meeting and the householders swore an oath of allegiance to their new street captain. For the next few weeks Albrecht's father used the two hours from sunset until curfew to meet with each of the neighbors.

In Nurnberg all the citizens were required to furnish their street captain with a list of their possessions that could be used in an emergency. Albrecht accompanied his father as he took account of arms, ammunition, spare rooms, ladders, lanterns, grain reserves and carts. He reported all that he found to the quartermaster who coordinated the lists and gave assignments to each neighborhood.

In their neighborhood of *Unter der Vesten,* fire hooks, leather buckets, ladders, and axes were mounted on certain houses on the block. Every man was expected to answer a summons when there was a fire. The quartermaster offered rewards to the first four carters to bring water to the fire and the first three men up the ladders. Albrecht dreamed of how exciting it would be to climb the ladders in a fire, but his father said he was too young.

Albrecht's father also had to maintain locked barrels filled with coils of iron chain. The chain was used to block the ends of the street in case of a riot.

Albrecht's father came home from his first street captain meeting to announce a new ordinance. Pigs would no longer be allowed to forage freely in the streets. They must be kept in pens. Albrecht thought with satisfaction that Hildebrand the pig would no longer be a menace.

One evening Albrecht sat by the fire while his dog, Hund, dozed near his feet. His sleek gray coat gleamed softly in the firelight and his majestic head rested lightly on his front paws. Albrecht lightly sketched the figure of his sleeping dog on a scrap of paper.

On the other side of the wide fireplace Willibald squinted at a small book. The fire did not provide enough light, but the Dürer household could not spare candles. Willibald rubbed his eyes and let the book fall to his lap. "What are you drawing?"

Albrecht held up the half-finished drawing. "A portrait of Hund."

Willibald admired the picture. "I wish I had a dog. My father says we cannot keep one because we travel too much. If I had a dog I would name him Phylax Noricus. I like "Noricus" because that was the Roman name of this area, and "Phylax" is a good name because that is the Greek word for Sentinel."

Albrecht laughed. "Hund is not much of a sentinel. He is getting so old that he would continue sleeping if a thief entered here!"

"But he is faithful!" replied Willibald. "Watch the way he follows your father everywhere. He even stays by his side in the workshop."

Albrecht returned to his sketch and made short strokes to

illustrate Hund's furry coat. "I think Hund would make a good Argos. Do you remember the story you told me of Odysseus's dog?"

Willibald leaned back in his chair. "Argos of the steadfast heart."

"I remember how even after all the years that Odysseus was away, Argos recognized him when no one else did."

"I have another story for you," said Willibald. "My tutor says that on the island of Salamis there is a mound known as the Dog's Mound. It is the tomb of the faithful dog of Xanthippus, the father of Pericles."

"Pericles was the great Greek leader you told me about," contributed Albrecht.

Willibald nodded. "Pericles told this story, and that is why we know it today. Someday I am going to explore the artifacts of Greece and Rome. My father says you can find coins from Roman times and the inscriptions..."

"What about the faithful dog?" interrupted Albrecht.

"It happened around 480 BC when Xanthippus and all the Athenians retreated to the Island of Salamis. They wanted to make the Persians fight them at sea. This faithful dog swam after his master's boat all the way across the strait. He was so exhausted when he arrived that he died. Xanthippus buried him and the Dog's Mound was famous for many years. I wonder if it would still be there."

Albrecht patted his own dog on the head. "You are a faithful dog," he whispered in Hund's ear. Hund stirred in his sleep and sighed with contentment.

Willibald spied the finished drawing. "Could I keep your picture of Hund? We are leaving for our other house tomorrow, but I would like to remember Hund."

"Of course you may have it," replied Albrecht. "And Hund and I will be faithfully waiting for you to return. You can pretend that you are Odysseus."

Willibald's eyes grew large in his round face. "Do you mean that I could pretend that Hund is my dog, too?"

"Yes, and you may call him Hund Noricus! He will sound very regal, don't you think?"

Portrait of a Knight, 1495, watercolor & pen

Chapter 4

"Something of all things I will know..."
Albrecht Dürer

Festival Week

Albrecht's mother bustled about the home, giving last minute directions to Ursula.

"While I am at church remember to put the bread in the oven, and don't let the baby play in the spinning."

Ursula promised she would take care of everything. Albrecht and Sebald had gotten permission to help in their father's shop. They tried to leave without their mother noticing, but she caught them before they even reached the stairs.

"Boys, you must do what your father tells you and do not make any trouble for the assistants and apprentices." She gave them a final inspection. Satisfied that their clothes and faces were clean, she kissed each of them on the forehead. "Go in the name of Christ," she said. The boys escaped at last to the ground floor where their father kept his workshop.

When they arrived in the shop, their cousin Niklas greeted them. Niklas was several years older than Albrecht and had almost completed his journeyman years. He was working on the "Master Piece" he would present to the guild for entrance as a Master Goldsmith.

"Your father left on business and told me to mind the shop," Niklas said. "He is often busy now that he is Official Assayer of Gold."

"What is an Official Assayer of Gold?" asked Sebald, trying to get his tongue around the long words.

"He is the one who weighs and gives a fair value to gold," replied Niklas. He looked at the boys curiously. "It is a very important position. Didn't your father tell you?"

Albrecht flushed with embarrassment. Niklas probably thought they were silly children.

Niklas saw Albrecht's expression and hastened to make amends. "Don't be embarrassed. It is your father's way. He does not want to boast."

Niklas brought out two work aprons and offered them to the boys. "I could use your help. There will be more traffic since the pilgrims are starting to arrive for Festival Week. Ask Jakob which chores are left for you."

Jakob was the youngest apprentice. He was only a few years older than Albrecht, but he considered himself to be much more experienced. He was sweeping, but when the boys approached he put aside his broom. "I will begin by teaching you what I have learned," he said airily. "First you must know that goldsmiths are very important." Jakob puffed out his chest like the bellows used to fan the coals in the brazier.

"Why?" asked Albrecht.

"Their skill is used to create things of beauty and instruments for scientists, even moveable type to print books." He nodded to Albrecht. "Your godfather Anton Koberger was a goldsmith until he became a printer."

"Will you be a goldsmith in Nurnberg, like Father?" asked Albrecht.

"No, I just came here for my apprenticeship. I will have to find work as a journeyman somewhere else. Then when I am a master, I can set up trade in a city that needs more goldsmiths."

Albrecht pondered this plan.

"Do you know why it is so important to learn in several places?" asked Jakob.

"I suppose you learn more," began Albrecht hesitantly.

"That is right! In fact the secrets of the trade are so important that a master craftsman must swear an oath of loyalty to his city every year so that he does not betray the secrets to outsiders."

"But you are an outsider," protested Albrecht.

"No, an apprentice or journeyman is an insider wherever he goes," replied Jakob. He laughed as though he were telling a clever joke.

"Back to sweeping!" called Niklas from the doorway of the shop. He worked outside the shop because of the city ordinance against open fires inside dwellings. He had a small brazier that he used to melt a small quantity of gold. Niklas motioned to the boys to come to his side. "Look, I will show you how to cast a small figure."

Albrecht and Sebald watched entranced while their cousin deftly made a small cross. Jacob finished his sweeping in time to see the finished ornament. "That cross is not so fancy," he said scornfully.

Niklas sighed. "It is easier to cast blame on a thing than to make it better," he said firmly. "As you get older I think you will find that simpler is often better."

Albrecht pondered his cousin's words. He had always loved ornate designs like those he saw at church each Sunday, but he remembered the stirring he felt when he looked at a perfectly-shaped leaf or the round shell of a nut. He wondered how a person could find beauty.

The next week Festival Week began. Festival Week fell on the Sunday after Easter every year. Thousands of pilgrims thronged the streets of Nurnberg for the viewing of the Emperor's Royal Treasures. The crowds were so large that the iron chains, which Albrecht's father and other street captains kept for emergencies, were stretched across the streets near the Market Square to direct the flow of traffic.

Willibald's family was in town, so Albrecht arranged to go to the festival with him. They planned to meet at a certain place on the Nurnberg city wall shortly after dawn. Albrecht waited at the top of the wall and watched as fingers of purplish light tinged the hillsides east of the city. Then the clouds turned to gold as the sun rose. A feeling of joy welled up inside of Albrecht. He had felt this way before when he saw the golden bird his father had made, or admired a particularly beautiful tree in the snow. He liked to think it was the feeling of beauty.

Willibald arrived shortly. He was breathing hard from the exertion of running the steps up to the wall. He brought raisin buns for their breakfast and a curious apple which swung from a string around his neck. "My mother made me wear this," he said dolefully. "It is stuffed with garlic and spices to keep off the plague." Albrecht took a sniff of the apple.

"Phew! It will keep away more than that!"

The gates of the city opened and the boys joined the crowd of pilgrims on their way to the Market Place. As they passed through the metalworking district, they stopped to look at the stalls of the needlemakers, silversmiths, cutlers, and nail makers. Albrecht peered into the shop where swords and armor were made. The finished coats of armor gleamed in their places on the walls. "I wish I could draw a real knight on a brave charger!" Albrecht said.

Willibald's eyes shone as brightly as the armor. "Perhaps we will see some soldiers today."

The boys enjoyed the sights and sounds of the festival. There were vendors selling sweets, trinkets, and pictures of the royal treasures. The pictures were made from crude wood blocks, and Albrecht lingered over them to see how they were drawn. "You can draw better than that," whispered Willibald. There were also beggars, wearing their badges to show that they were licensed to beg by the city of Nurnberg.

By careful maneuvering the boys at last reached a spot near the edges of the Market Place. A wooden tower had been built in the middle of the open square. To the delight of both boys, heavily armed soldiers stood around the base to protect the Royal Treasures.

"That sword must weigh thirty pounds..." began Albrecht enthusiastically.

Suddenly trumpets sounded and a hush fell over the crowd.

"The Imperial Regalia of the Holy Roman Empire," shouted a rich baritone voice.

Albrecht and Willibald watched as a procession of men solemnly mounted the platform at the top of the tower.

Royal officers came forward one by one to display the coronation regalia, which included the jeweled crown and gleaming sword of Charlemagne. There were also the crown jewels, a scepter and orb, and coronation robe. Albrecht had seen the treasures each year since he was old enough to sit on his father's shoulders. His favorite part was the showing of the Holy Relics.

As Albrecht watched, the Bishop of Bamberg led a host of priests who carried the Holy Relics up the stairs to the top of the tower. The Bishop, in his richly ornamented robe, raised his arm over the crowd and pronounced a blessing.

The crowd seemed to hold its breath as each of the holy relics was raised high. There were the Holy Lance that pierced Christ's side, a piece of the cross encased in a beautiful reliquary, a splinter of the manger, a piece of the tablecloth from the Last Supper and many other objects. Many people made the motion of the cross, and Albrecht noticed that the man next to him moved his mouth as though silently praying.

The priests holding the treasures descended from the platform and paraded around the square three times. Then a cleric announced the indulgences rewarded for viewing the relics.

"Those who view these relics are released from thirty-seven years and 275 days of Purgatory," he intoned in a hollow voice.

Albrecht was barely ten years old. Thirty-seven years sounded like a long time. Then he remembered what his father had told him about eternal salvation. Eternal meant forever. Thirty-seven years was not so long as that.

Study for the Hands of an Apostle

Chapter 5

*"And who loves God with all his heart Chooses the wise
and better part."*
Albrecht Dürer

The Plague

A lbrecht settled his baby sister in a soft patch of dandelions
and guided her plump fingers to touch one of the yellow flowers. Albrecht was apprenticed to his father, but he still enjoyed
helping his mother with the youngest children.

"See how soft it is, Catherine." Albrecht picked the curling leaf
of a dandelion and tickled her chin. The baby chortled with delight
and swiftly grabbed the leaf and put it in her mouth. She had the
same curly blond hair of her older brother. She seemed to have the
same curiosity for nature as well.

"No, not in your mouth," said Albrecht. The baby responded by
clutching Albrecht's finger.

Peter was playing nearby with a pile of wood shavings he had
collected. He came to lean on Albrecht's shoulder. "Play wif me,"
he commanded his older brother.

Albrecht dug in his pockets and found a folded piece of
parchment, a stick of charcoal, and two white feathers. "Look at
these feathers," he told Peter. "They are from the birds that live in
St. Sebald's Cathedral."

Peter reverently touched a feather. "Birds," he said softly.

"God gave birds feathers so they can fly." Skillfully Albrecht
drew the outline of a bird on the parchment. "When you draw a

bird you must look at every feather." With Catherine still clutching a finger of his left hand, Albrecht gently guided Peter's clumsy fingers as he colored along the lines of a feather.

When the bird was finished, Peter held the drawing for Catherine to see. "Me do it!" he announced proudly. Catherine gurgled in reply.

One morning a few weeks later, Albrecht awoke to feel an ache in every joint of his body. His head felt swollen and hot. He opened his eyes slowly, but the room swirled around him, then turned black. The next time he awoke his mother was leaning over him.

"How are you feeling, son?"

His mother's voice seemed to come from far away, but Albrecht could see her hands near his face. Her palms were pressed together in prayer. While the room remained a blur, Albrecht focused on his mother's hands. Her long fingers lightly touched one another. How many times had he seen her hands like this, and always the care-worn hands were beautiful to Albrecht.

"Albrecht, can you speak?" his mother asked anxiously.

His voice, when he spoke, came out more like a croak. "Yes, but I am thirsty."

His mother brought him a cup of water and tenderly wiped his feverish brow. "Sleep as much as you can," she said. "I must go to Catherine now."

A stab of worry pierced Albrecht's heart. "Catherine is sick, too?"

His mother nodded through her tears, then hurried from the room.

Albrecht slept restlessly. He thought he heard cries and bells. Always his head ached and the room swirled when he opened his eyes. He was dimly aware of his mother bringing him cups of water, and once he awakened enough to hear a priest praying. He was too weary to wonder if he was going to die.

At last the morning arrived when Albrecht awoke to see sunshine filtering through his tightly drawn shutters. The room no longer moved around him. His head felt light, and he was strangely hungry. His mother sat motionless in the corner of the room. Her head was bent, her hands folded in her lap. She looked up when she heard Albrecht stir. Her face was gaunt, and the usually luminous eyes were sunken and dark.

A sudden fear gripped Albrecht. "Mother, where is Catherine?"

His mother began to weep. Albrecht's father entered the room. He clasped Albrecht's hand. "The doctor says you will get better," he said. He tried to continue, but his voice choked. He held his son's hand while tears streamed down his cheeks.

"Father, where is Catherine?"

"She has gone to heaven," his father whispered.

A feeling of loss swept over Albrecht. In his mind he could see his little sister toddling after him, and feel her chubby arms clinging trustingly to him. When he thought of his sister, he felt an ache in his heart that would never go away.

After a long recovery Albrecht resumed his apprenticeship with his father. He was in his second year and strove to learn all that he could. His father taught him how to work with precious metals and how to use the burin to engrave intricate designs.

Albrecht had such a steady hand that his father taught him how to make silverpoint drawings with the burin. He used the sharp point of the burin to scratch the surface of specially prepared paper. The paper had a silver coating and the burin would leave a mark that darkened over time. With silver point drawing no corrections could be made.

Albrecht and his father vied with one another to make the most life-like self portraits. Albrecht's father was surprised at his son's ability to copy from life.

The new technique awakened in Albrecht a new interest. Though he spent his days executing trade designs, his thoughts roamed to how to create beauty in his art.

One day he asked his father how to discern real beauty. His father considered his answer for a moment. "I have always thought that true beauty is hidden in creation and it is the artists' job to find it."

Albrecht applied himself to learn his craft so well that he could find the true beauty. As he completed his third year of apprenticeship his father assigned him a costly drinking cup to make for a customer.

The sun set late in the summer, and on this summer evening

Albrecht and his father were working unusually late. At last Albrecht's father placed his burin on the table and removed his work apron. His dog raised his shaggy, gray head and eyed him wearily. "Hund is tired, and I think it must be time to close the shop."

Albrecht looked up from the delicate cup that he was inscribing. "Father, could you look at this for me? I want it to be the finest quality."

Albrecht's father took the cup in his hands and held it to the dimming window light. He studied it for a long time. "This is the finest work you have done yet," he said quietly. "Your hand is steady. The proportions are beautiful to see. Do you love your craft, Albrecht?"

Albrecht looked into his father's shining eyes and hesitated. How could he tell him what was really in his heart? "I love it more than eating and sleeping."

His father nodded with satisfaction. "That is how I was, too. I even left my father's workshop because I loved the craft he gave me so much." The older man stared through the window, as though seeing into another time, another place. "I wanted to learn even more. He understood, so he let me go—first to the Netherlands where the art flourished at the highest level. Then to Nurnberg where a craftsman could be free to develop his art..."

"Father, I love art the same way!" Albrecht spoke quickly for fear he would stop before the words were said. "I want to learn the art of painting."

Albrecht's father ran his finger over the delicate engraving on the gold cup. "When I saw your work, I knew you wanted something more." He was quiet for a long time. At last he said, "I will find a master to teach you painting. Only I wish these years had not been wasted."

"No father! They have not been wasted! I have learned what it means to be an artist first from you."

The older man looked tenderly upon his young son. Barely thirteen years of age, yet so full of vigor.

"You will be a fine painter," he said softly.

Chapter 6

"It is art acquired and learned from God's creation, which sows, waxes and bears fruit after its kind."
Albrecht Dürer

The Painter's Apprentice

A neighborhood cock crowed in the dim light of a raw November morning as Albrecht made his way to the workshop of Michael Wolgemut, painter. A sprightly man with penetrating green eyes met him at the door.

"Welcome to my apprenticeship." He spoke and moved quickly, as he ushered Albrecht into the workshop and introduced him to the other assistants, journeymen, and apprentices, who were already at work.

Albrecht looked with wonder at the many works of art that the men were making.

"This is the Augustinerkirche altarpiece," Herr Wolgemut said with a wave of his hand. Albrecht had a glimpse of a large planed board being painted with white, before his new master led him away to another corner.

He saw boys about his own age mixing pigments in bowls while several painters added details to a lavish landscape. "This is my step-son Wilhelm Pleydenwuff," Herr Wolgemut said as the oldest of the painters stepped forward to meet Albrecht. "He handles commissions with princes and bishops." Albrecht detected a trace of pride in his voice.

In a third corner assistants carved blocks of wood with sharply pointed tools. "And these will be wood cut engravings on order from Anton Koberger, the prince of printers."

"I know him. He is my god-father."

Herr Wolgemut smiled. "He is my friend, and so is your father. I hold them both in great respect. They say that I must make a great painter of you. What do you say to that?"

Albrecht looked at the busy activity around him and knew that he could be happy here. "I will do my best, sir."

"Good. You will begin by learning to mix pigments." The master painter called one of the younger boys and gave him instructions to teach Albrecht the duties of an apprentice.

The boy introduced himself as Johann. He had sandy-colored hair, a snub nose and a voice that cracked when he talked. He had only begun to show Albrecht the bowls of pigment when one of the assistants called for more wood for the fire. "That is our job," said Johann. "Follow me and I will show you where the wood is kept."

Albrecht followed Johann through a dizzying list of chores. They brought water, cleaned brushes, mixed pigments, and a dozen other duties. As the daylight faded, the painters had to leave their work. Johann and Albrecht swept the floor carefully, so that no dust would mar the paintings. Only Herr Wolgemut remained.

"How did you like your first day as an apprentice?" he asked.

Albrecht flexed his aching fingers. For a moment he thought of the satisfying work he had done in his father's shop, but he dismissed such thoughts from his mind. "I learned that I have much to learn," he said.

Herr Wolgemut's eyes twinkled. "It will not always be work. Come again tomorrow and learn some more."

The next few months contained a steady round of hard work at the Wolgemut studio. The artists and apprentices worked six days a week from sunrise, which marked the first hour of the day on Nurnberg's Great Clock, to sunset. Interspersed with chores Albrecht had the opportunity to watch the artists at work. He learned that most of the artwork prepared in the workshop was designed by Herr Wolgemut. The apprentices faithfully copied his designs onto the larger canvases or boards.

Like the goldsmith's art, painting was an anonymous craft. It did not matter that several painters worked on a single painting. It would simply be considered a product of the Wolgemut workshop.

The chief assistant who cut the wood blocks showed Albrecht how they were made. He was older than Albrecht's father and his wrinkled face wreathed in a smile when he noted Albrecht's interest.

"You say you have already served apprentice to a goldsmith?"

"Yes, under my father."

"Then you will find my craft to be similar to your own." The man carefully chose a block of wood. He swept his hand along its smooth white surface. "A woodcut is a relief print. Do you see how we sawed this block of wood along the grain and covered it with a white paint?"

Albrecht nodded.

The old man held up a second block. "Next we draw a picture on it with ink like this design."

Albrecht saw a simple picture of the Virgin Mary holding the infant Jesus. He had seen similar pictures printed on cards that were sold at fairs in Nurnberg.

The artist drew out a sharp tool and began to gently gouge the wood. "My job is to cut away the wood from either side of the lines that were drawn. Then, when we apply ink to the ridges which are left and press it onto paper, it makes a print!"

Albrecht watched the delicate curls of wood fall to the floor as the chief assistant skillfully carved the wood block. As the carving progressed, the design looked less and less like the original drawing and more like a miniature sculpture.

"Do you see how I make some of the areas deeper than others?" he asked in a hoarse whisper. "That is my secret. It gives depth to the picture. None of the others can do it the way I do! They are still cutting the old way."

"What is the old way?" asked Albrecht.

"The old way was used for simple outlines that were colored in with water colors after they were printed by hand. The new prints are more intricate and are printed with presses." He proudly held up the finished woodcut. "These books we are designing will be the first created by an artist rather than a publisher. Herr Wolgemut says our goal is to give the world real art!"

The painters also liked to talk about their work and how they created certain effects. Albrecht realized that much of his new trade was dependent on what could be passed down from more experienced artists. Albrecht performed countless chores for these men, and was able to learn by watching them work.

One particularly gifted artist was named Klaus. He liked to talk while he worked, and was glad to answer Albrecht's questions. Klaus was the first man Albrecht had ever seen with a beard. Albrecht thought the unusual style made Klaus look wise, like the pictures of ancient saints. He wondered what it would be like to wear a beard. The artist surprised his young friend by painting a small portrait of Albrecht into the Augustinerkirche altarpiece.

Though Albrecht made several friends among the assistants and journeymen, most of the young apprentices took delight in teasing him. Only Johann remained a true friend. He did what he could to protect Albrecht from their pranks. Despite his aid, Albrecht had to endure blackened brushes, hidden water buckets and mysterious heaps of sawdust that appeared after he had swept the floor.

When Herr Wolgemut gave his lessons, however, Albrecht forgot these irritations. He concentrated his entire energies on learning how to handle the pen and brush, how to copy a picture accurately, and how to paint with water color and oil paint. Herr Wolgemut observed the accuracy of Albrecht's hand, and took an increasing interest in the young artist.

One summer evening in 1487 the longer daylight hours permitted the painters to work later than usual. Albrecht was assigned to copy one of Herr Wolgemut's illustrations onto a wood block. His practiced hand deftly outlined the picture from the small drawing onto the larger block. Herr Wolgemut stopped to inspect Albrecht's work.

"You have the engraver's eye and hand," he said.

Albrecht looked up in surprise. "My father taught me this way."

"You can learn a lot with a hand like that, for first an artist must learn from the great artists that have come before them.

When you accurately copy great art you are receiving a private art lesson from a master. But do you know who the greatest art master is?"

Albrecht studied his wood block for a moment. "My father always said that the greatest artist was the Creator."

Herr Wolgemut laughed. "Your father has taught you well. I think you are ready to learn from the Greatest Art Master."

Albrecht looked confused.

"It is time for you to draw from nature," Herr Wolgemut declared. "I want you to draw and paint real landscapes, real objects."

View of Nuremburg from the West, 1495-97

A Portrait of Michael Wolgemut, 1516

Chapter 7

"It is easier to cast blame on a thing than to make it better."
Albrecht Dürer

A Portrait for Father

A lbrecht squinted at the wire drawing mill in the distance, and then looked back at the watercolor picture on his lap. "This picture looks lopsided."

Johann looked from his own painting and studied Albrecht's picture critically. "I think the problem is that it slopes to the left here," he said, pointing to the lower left corner. "It is still much better than mine. I cannot even show this to Herr Wolgemut."

"Then I will not show him mine, either," replied Albrecht.

"No, you must show your painting!"

Albrecht was surprised by his friend's forcefulness.

Johann continued. "Don't you understand that you are different from the rest of us? That is why the other apprentices make fun of you. They are jealous because they know they will never be able to paint like you."

"Johann, you paint a true line."

"No, I am simply a draftsman. I can copy the design I am given, but you have the eye to create real art. Why do you think Herr Wolgemut asked to keep the painting you made of the cemetery of St. John. It was real art!"

Albrecht fell silent. The soft summer breeze brought the sound of the gurgling stream. "All I ever wanted to do was paint and draw. I never thought that others would dislike me for it."

Johann laughed and the somber mood was broken. "There are many of us who like you. With a gift like yours you must accept that some people will be jealous!"

In the days that followed Albrecht spent the earliest hours of the day outside the studio. In the morning when the hills around Nurnberg flushed with purple and the dew still sparkled on the grass, Albrecht felt the old feeling of delight rising inside him. "If only I could capture this beauty," he would murmur to himself. His eyes hungrily drank in every detail as he drew landscapes and objects from nature.

One morning he returned from an assignment to hear angry voices from behind one of the large altarpieces.

"I will not permit the portrait of the Pope in this painting!" declared a voice that could only belong to Herr Wolgemut.

"But you cannot have the adoration of the Virgin Mary without the Pope," shot back the fiery voice of an assistant.

"The Pope that we have now is making a mockery of his office," replied Herr Wolgemut. "You may portray the righteous popes of the past, but not this... this...donkey!"

Albrecht heard a gasp, and then he was confronted with the red face of the assistant as he strode out the studio door.

Albrecht hurried to collect the assistant's painting supplies before the paint should dry and ruin the brushes. Herr Wolgemut motioned him to stop. He personally took up the brushes and replaced the face of the would-be Pope with the mild countenance of a saintly old man.

"I think a portrait of St. Sebald will do nicely here," he explained with a tight smile. With short, deft strokes he finished the portrait.

Albrecht could not restrain his curiosity. "Sir, you do not respect the Pope?"

Herr Wolgemut looked at his young apprentice quizzically. "Your father is a pious man. Does he not tell you of the terrible curse that has come upon the church?"

"No, sir."

Herr Wolgemut produced a large book from the shelf. "This is the Holy Bible in Latin. Can you read it?"

"I have learned some Latin."

"Good. Then you must take it and study the Word of God. You will see how the pope has made a mockery of the revelation of God. What has your father taught you about God?"

Albrecht thought hard. "He always teaches us to fear God, be thankful, and work to be pleasing to God and man."

"And what has your father taught you about the Savior Jesus?"

"That he is the only way of salvation by his death on the cross."

Herr Wolgemut nodded his head in agreement, and his hazel eyes flashed. "That is the most important lesson you will ever learn. The recent popes have led the church to deny this simple truth and to teach that man is saved by works and empty rituals. You will find the truth in the Holy Bible. A true artist must know the scriptures if he would paint truly."

The years of Albrecht's apprenticeship quickly passed. His final assignment from Herr Wolgemut was a portrait of his father. Albrecht's father sat proudly at his workbench while his son painted his portrait.

"This will be a present for Mother," Albrecht said as he carefully painted the curling wisps of his father's hair.

"Then you must make a portrait of your mother for me," his father countered.

"Only if you will sit still. I can see that you are trying to finish that ornament when I am not looking!"

"I thought the truly fine artists could paint while the subject was moving," teased his father.

"I am not a fine artist yet."

Albrecht's father grew quiet. He was still for a few minutes. "You will leave for your journeyman studies soon. Your mother

Portrait of the Artist's Father

will greatly miss you, I fear."

"I will miss you, too," replied Albrecht. "I owe you a debt I can never repay."

His father waved his words aside. "We are proud of your hard work. Your studies as a journeyman are important for the rest of your life's work. Keep your eyes and ears open and learn as much as you can."

Albrecht studied his father's eyes for a moment. They held the far-seeing expression he had seen so often on his father's face.

"Herr Koberger's book-delivery convoy leaves after Easter," continued his father. "I have arranged for you to travel with them to Mainz and then to Colmar, where you will study with Martin Schongauer. He is the finest painter and engraver in the realm. After you have learned what you can from him, I would recommend going to Basle. It is the center of publishing in Europe, and you will find Herr Schongauer's brother, Georg, there." His father sighed. "I remember my own journeyman years. There is so much to learn."

Albrecht put the final touches to his father's eyes. It was an excellent likeness.

A few weeks later Albrecht began his journeyman studies. Anton Koberger, Albrecht's godfather, personally traveled with the convoy that Albrecht joined. The convoy was escorted by armed guards since renegade knights and bandits stalked the forests and countryside around Nurnberg. During the trip, Herr Koberger talked with Albrecht about the printing business.

"Printing has great potential for a talented young artist," he told Albrecht. "Artwork that is printed can be enjoyed by thousands of people. The art can travel to faraway cities. A fancy altarpiece cannot do that!"

"But an altarpiece is a work of art that will last through the centuries," protested Albrecht.

Herr Koberger fixed him with an appraising eye. "A print can be a work of art for the ages as well, if it is done by a true artist."

Albrecht took his godfather's words to heart and applied himself to study printing as well as painting. In Mainz his father and Herr Koberger had given him letters of introduction to a talented Dutch artist who hired him to work in his studio on both paintings and woodcuts.

After a year and a half he traveled with another book convoy to Colmar where he was to work for Martin Schongauer. Sadly, the great artist had died shortly before Albrecht's arrival. Two of his brothers were running the workshop. They hired Albrecht to work for them and study the great artist's works. When Albrecht had learned all he could, he traveled on to Basel where he was to work for Georg Schongauer.

Georg Schongauer let out a low whistle as he studied the sketches Albrecht brought him. "Where did you learn to design wood blocks like this? The illustration is well-suited to be carved into wood, and the use of texture is quite novel."

"I studied under Michael Wolgemut."

The printer nodded, lost in thought. "I believe I have the perfect assignment for you. I need an illustration for a volume of letters by Saint Jerome. They say you cannot judge a book by its cover, but whenever I introduce illustrations to a book the sales increase ten-fold."

Albrecht set to work at once. In keeping with the popular stories about Jerome, he sketched the saint nursing the paw of a lion. Since he had never seen a real lion, he used a lion he had seen in a painting once.

Albrecht also wanted to show the importance of Jerome's work in translating the Bible into Latin. He sketched an open book and copied the first words of Genesis 1:1 from the Latin Bible. The picture still looked too bare. With a sudden inspiration, he added two more open books. He would find someone who could give him the first words of Genesis 1:1 in Greek and Hebrew. With fresh resolve, Albrecht refined his illustration.

Herr Schongauer praised the illustration and insisted that

Albrecht put his name on it. Albrecht used a Latinized form of his name, and added "Noricus," the word Willibald had taught him was the Roman word for the Nurnberg area.

When the *Letters of St. Jerome* was printed, Albrecht's illustration was widely praised. Orders for more illustrations flowed to Herr Schongauer. Two sets of illustrations were for collections of stories for children. Albrecht enjoyed illustrating the morals of the fanciful tales. There were stories showing the foolishness of pride, laziness, and astrology.

St. Jerome in his study, 1492

One afternoon Albrecht was putting the finishing touches to a design of a fool rushing to put out his neighbor's fire while his own house burned. Albrecht answered a knock at the door and found a messenger with a letter from his father.

Albrecht read the letter carefully. His father's perfect script ran across the page in lines so straight that one would think he had used a ruler. He wrote of the family. In the years since Albrecht had left home his mother

Fool and his Neighbor's Fire

had born two more children. Father wrote to tell of the birth of his eighteenth child: a son named Carl.

In his letter he also told of a great honor he received. The Emperor Friedrich III had asked him to come to his castle at Linz in order to commission a drinking vessel. His father had been the guest of the Emperor! The letter contained another surprise. His father requested a portrait of Albrecht to be given to the family of his proposed bride!

Self Portrait at 22

"Painting is a useful art when it is of a godly sort and employed for holy edification."
Albrecht Dürer

Mein Agnes

It was 1493 and Albrecht was twenty-two years old. He sat before a mirror and tried to paint the portrait his father had requested. Albrecht dabbed the brush in paint. What should he show in his painting?

Three years of journeyman work had slipped by quickly. He was now a skilled artist, who had been employed to make woodcut illustrations for books. He had learned much in the trade of engraving and printing. He had also studied painting and prepared a large portfolio of his work. He knew his father would be proud of his hard work, but is that who he really was?

Albrecht cast a critical eye at the painting before him. He saw a young man with blond hair, high cheekbones, and the beginnings of a wispy beard. He wore a hat jauntily perched on his head in the fashion of Strasbourg where he was currently staying.

With sudden inspiration, Albrecht began to paint the delicate leaves of a sprig of Eryngium. The plant was a symbol of fidelity and love. That was the message he wanted to send home to his future bride. Above the painting he wrote the words: "My affairs are determined by what is written high above." Satisfied with the painting, he left the parchment to dry. He would copy the painting onto vellum and send it to his father with the next Koberger book convoy.

A drawing of Agnes Dürer

On the Monday before St. Margaret's Day, July 7, 1494 Albrecht married Agnes Frey. Agnes was the daughter of a successful goldsmith. In the few weeks Albrecht had known her, he realized that she had a keen business sense. Albrecht admired the delicate chin and clear blue eyes of his bride. He thought she would make a beautiful subject for a painting.

The young couple set up their first home in his parents' house, but shortly afterwards a plague struck. Albrecht remembered the plague that had taken his little sister. He vowed that his new wife would be protected from danger. Thus, only a few months after their marriage, Albrecht took Agnes to live with her relatives in the safety of the countryside.

The small village did not provide work for an artist. Reluctantly Albrecht departed for Italy, where he would be able to both earn a living and further study the new renaissance art.

Albrecht carried with him a sketch he had made of "Mein Agnes" as he called her. It showed her with bowed head, lost in thought, her pig tail swinging loosely down her back. He hoped it would not be long before they would be reunited.

Venice, the city of Saint Mark, glittered with well-dressed men and women from many countries. There were colorful Italian gentlewomen in high-waisted dresses, jewel merchants from India, Turkish gentlemen in turbans, oriental alchemists, Circassian slave girls with their elaborate headdresses, and richly-dressed bankers from Germany.

Albrecht soon met several Italian artists. Whether successful or not, they dressed like gentlemen. Albrecht wondered how they supported themselves, since many of them wiled away their time with other interests like dancing and music. He did not understand some of the youngest artists, who carried themselves with the air of men who were bored with life.

For Albrecht life in Venice was anything but boring. He relished the new sights and sounds. Venice was built on dozens of small islands that were connected by bridges. The Venetians used canals instead of streets.

The Grand Canal was the main thoroughfare. It wound through the city like a sinuous snake, and intersected the smaller canals. Albrecht saw boatmen who were called gondoliers. They transported passengers in flat-bottomed boats with elegantly-shaped high prows.

Willibald

Splendid palaces lined the banks of the canals. On one of the palaces Albrecht saw a sculpture of a lion. As he studied the majestic animal, he laughed at the thought of the lion he had drawn for the illustration of St. Jerome. By comparison his lion looked like an overgrown poodle! He made some hasty sketches of the stone lions.

Albrecht saw a lobster for the first time. He surprised the seafood merchant by standing at his booth for an hour to draw the novel creature.

During his first month in Italy, Albrecht's old friend Willibald Pirckheimer paid him a visit. Willibald was studying classical languages at the University of Pavia in Italy. He arrived, covered with the pale Italian dust, one afternoon as Albrecht was finishing a water color painting.

He thumped at his dusty cloak, then enveloped his friend in a great embrace. "Albrecht, I got your letter that you were coming to Italy! I am so pleased to find you here!"

"It is good to see a familiar face in all these new things," replied Albrecht.

Willibald laughed. "But your face is not so familiar. I see you have grown a beard."

Albrecht self-consciously stroked his beard, which had grown thicker since he arrived in Italy. "My mother will still not accept it, but I have decided that I will wear a beard."

Willibald squinted at his friend in an appraising manner. "It suits you. It is a little eccentric, but no one will ever forget the bearded artist!"

Willibald's quick eyes glanced around the room and came to rest on the water color picture. "What is this?"

"It is a study I am making of a lobster."

"A lobster? Surely there are more beautiful subjects in Italy than a lobster!"

"Perhaps, but none so interesting. My father may never see a live lobster, but he will enjoy seeing a picture of one."

"And what is this?" Willibald pointed to a small monogram of an A and D at the bottom of the picture. "Is the A and D short for anno domini, the year of our Lord?"

"No, it is the new style in Italy to sign your work with your initials."

His friend studied the monogram for another moment. "Albrecht, I believe that you will go down in history as a great artist. It is the spirit of the age— a time that is ripe for men to express themselves as individuals. Your father made beautiful things with his craft, but he never signed even one. You will be different."

Albrecht grew quiet. "My father taught me that art is a gift from God. I want to show that we can see beauty in nature because God is the creator."

Willibald raised an eyebrow in surprise. "You have advanced in your reading of the Bible since I saw you last."

"Yes, I am finishing my second reading, and I have a new project based on the Revelation of John. Here are some of my ideas."

Albrecht eagerly described the details of his project. Willibald had also studied the book of Revelation, and added his knowledge of classical languages to Albrecht's research.

"It will be the year 1500 in only a few years. Many people think the end of the world will come. There is much interest in the Revelation of John," said Albrecht.

As Willibald prepared to leave, he grinned. "I will be interested to see how you portray the Pope. Has Herr Wolgemut converted you to his way of thinking?"

"That will require much study," replied Albrecht.

Chapter 9

"Seeing that through disobedience of sin we have fallen into everlasting Death, no help could have reached us save through the incarnation of the Son of God, whereby He through His innocent suffering might abundantly pay thee Father all our guilt, so that the Justice of God might be satisfied."
Albrecht Dürer

The Apocalypse

T he coach bumped over a rut, and Albrecht protectively placed himself between Agnes and the flimsy door. Agnes had grown more beautiful since he had seen her last. Albrecht had to keep reminding himself that this modest young woman with the large eyes was his own wife.

"We will arrive in Nurnberg soon," he assured her. "Do you think you can make the last few hours?"

Agnes looked pale, but she nodded bravely. Albrecht tried to distract her with some conversation.

"I have planned my master work, and I think it is going to provide us with a good income," he began.

"Is it a painting?" asked Agnes timidly.

"It is like a painting, because it will be an original work of art. But I will not use paint. I have a plan to make a series of woodcuts like no one has ever made before!"

Agnes looked doubtful. Even when she felt sick, her strong business sense asserted itself. "But how will you find a publisher to produce your idea?"

"Darling, I am going to be my own publisher."

Agnes sat stunned for a moment. Albrecht took her hand in his. "I know we can make it work. My father will let me use his workshop at first. I have already made the first designs. I will carve them myself so that they will have the texture I want. They will be larger than other woodcuts, too."

"But how will you print them?"

"My godfather, Anton Koberger will lend me the typefaces and bind the books for me. He will recognize it is a good investment. Look, here is the first design. They will all be illustrations of the last book of the Bible."

As Albrecht showed her the details of his pictures from the book of Revelation, Agnes grew interested despite herself.

"I want these prints to show the truth of God's word to those who cannot read," Albrecht explained. "When they see the judgment of God they will want to repent of their sins and seek God."

Agnes studied the detailed illustrations before her. "These are certainly unlike anything Nurnberg has ever seen," she said softly. "There is a lot of fear now, too. People fear the world will end when the year 1500 arrives." She smoothed her skirts and nodded with finality. "We will do it. God has not given us children yet so I can help."

"Ah, *mein* Agnes," said Albrecht, using his pet name for her. "You will see that God will be honored in our hard work."

For the next several months Albrecht hardly ate or slept while he worked on the *Apocalypse*, as he called it. The illustrations required much study of the Bible. At the same time, religious problems were brewing in the church of Rome.

Albrecht's old master, Herr Wolgemut, had made a controversial wood cut of the pope shown as a donkey. He often visited Albrecht, and his green eyes clouded with worry as he denounced the sins of the current pope.

Slowly, the *Apocalypse* took form. Periodically Albrecht made test impressions of the wood cuts to check how the carvings appeared on paper. His skills from his goldsmith years gave him a steady, sure hand with the wood. At last the sequence of fifteen illustrations was complete.

Albrecht arranged for the Bible text to be printed on the

The Fifth Seal

opposite side of his illustrations. He did not want the illustrations to go without the words of the Bible because God revealed Himself in the Bible and the words themselves were holy. When he showed the first bound volume of the *Apocalypse* to Agnes, she glowed

The Four Horsemen

with a quiet delight. Carefully she turned each page.

"Master Koberger said they will sell like ginger cakes at the next fair. Herr Imhoff will also export them to other cities for sale," she told Albrecht.

She studied one print in particular. "This fifth print is very powerful," said Agnes. "Is this the pope here?"

"Yes, this shows the fifth and sixth seals being opened and the vials of wrath are being poured on the unrighteous."

"But, Albrecht, this is the pope being judged!"

Albrecht studied the figure wearing the pope's pointed hat. "It is sad to see judgment, but there are many people who have abused power and never truly come to God. See, the judgment is upon a cardinal, bishop, kaiser and kaiserin as well!"

"But what if a cardinal or bishop sees this print?"

"*Mein* Agnes, I hope that they will see it," said Albrecht stoutly. "I hope they will repent of their sins before it is too late."

The *Apocalypse* was a great success. Albrecht used his own press and typefaces borrowed from his godfather Anton Koberger. He did not slacken his work pace to enjoy his success. Instead he doubled his efforts to produce another series of illustrations.

Albrecht had a rough plan for two more woodcut series and several series of engravings based on a technique he had developed with Herr Wolgemut. The engravings would be more expensive, but could be marketed to a wealthier clientele. Albrecht hoped to experiment with mythical themes and the lessons he had learned on proportion in Italy.

At about this time an artist named Jacopo dei Barberi came through Nurnberg. He asked to meet Albrecht. The two men found they had a common interest in the study of proportion. Jacopo showed Albrecht a drawing of a man and a woman that he said was based on a special canon of proportions. He would not divulge the secret of these proportions to Albrecht. Albrecht became more determined to learn the art of proportion so that he could share these secrets with other artists.

One afternoon an official page brought a letter to Albrecht. Agnes was at his side and could hardly contain herself as Albrecht carefully broke the wax seal and unfolded the parchment.

"It is from Elector Frederick of Saxony," said Albrecht with a touch of awe in his voice. "He wishes me to paint an altarpiece for him. It is to be the Virgin Mary and Jesus."

Agnes covered her mouth with her hand. "A painting!" she gasped.

Albrecht's eyes shone in anticipation. "It will be my first large work as my own master. We are ready to move into our own workshop and our own home."

A few months later the Dürers moved into their first home. They set up their workshop, complete with shelves for pigments and tools, a printer's workbench for mixing and applying ink, easels for paintings, and even a new puppy. Albrecht and Agnes adopted a homeless dog who appeared at their door one night. The puppy had a smooth brown coat and small lop ears.

Albrecht laughed when he first saw him. "He is nothing like my old dog Hund! I think he must be a mixture of all the dogs in Nurnberg."

"We will call him Franz and he will be a good watchdog," Agnes declared. She fed the small creature from her hand, and Franz became devoted to his mistress. However, he saved his greatest devotion for Albrecht. While Agnes bustled around the home or workshop with a dozen chores, Franz sat at Albrecht's feet while he painted.

To develop his market for portraiture, Albrecht decided to paint a self-portrait as a sample for his clients. Franz took great interest in the painting and trotted behind his master when he took it out to the yard to dry. Albrecht assumed the dog would follow him back into the house. He turned in time to see Franz plant a kiss on the cheek of the portrait!

Albrecht took pains to train Franz not to touch the paintings after this incident. In time Franz became so patient that Albrecht was even able to paint a young hare from the window without a sound from Franz. When the painting was completed Franz sniffed it suspiciously.

A Young Hare

A Piece of Turf

Chapter 10

*"Into whomsoever Christ comes he lives, and himself lives
in Christ. Therefore all things are in Christ good things."*
Albrecht Dürer

The Portrait of Grass

A gnes managed the workshop well, and Albrecht's brother
Hans became his first apprentice. Albrecht received
commissions to paint portraits of several prominent citizens.
Agnes said that they wanted their own paintings because they so
admired the local portraits that Albrecht had placed among those
bound for heaven in his *Apocalypse* illustrations! Willibald
returned from Italy and was a frequent guest at the Dürer home.
He claimed that Albrecht's reputation had reached all the way to
Italy where his *Apocalypse* was a great success.

Albrecht was glad that at last he could provide a secure home
for Agnes. His only concern was his father's health which
appeared to be failing.

One evening Albrecht's mother sent for him. His father had
become so ill that she feared he would die soon. Albrecht found his
father lying in bed. He was very weak, but managed to speak a
few words.

In a voice barely above a whisper, he said, "It is time." Albrecht
began to protest, but his father shook his head. "Trust in God," he
said firmly. "Live to please God."

The priest arrived and administered the Holy Sacraments.
When he left, Albrecht's father was too weak to talk. Albrecht held

his hand and talked to him late into the evening. He told his father of the new commission he had received to paint the Paumgartner Altarpiece. His father seemed to smile as he described how he would arrange the Nativity scene with rows of portraits of the donor and his family on either side.

Albrecht had one more thing that he needed to tell his father. "You have been a good father to me and a good master," he began. He stopped as he tried to keep a sob from rising in his throat. "Father, you taught me well, and I will pass on the art you taught me."

His father tried to speak, but his voice was so faint that Albrecht had to bend over him to hear. He heard his father whisper, "Your mother..."

"I will take care of Mother," Albrecht promised. His father relaxed and closed his eyes as if he would sleep. Albrecht stayed by his side until his mother came.

"You must get some sleep," she urged. "I will be nearby and can get you if he wakens."

Albrecht slept fitfully and near midnight a pounding on the door brought him fully awake. It was the maid with the news that his father was dying. Albrecht ran to his father's room and found his mother weeping. His father slept in the final sleep of death. Albrecht mourned that he had not been worthy to be with his father at the end.

Albrecht stayed with his mother for the next few days. There were so many details to manage that he scarcely had time to feel his own grief. He invited Hans to live with him. His brother Endres was the only one of his brothers who was apprenticed to his father. He arranged for him to finish his apprenticeship under their cousin Niklas. He tried to convince his mother to live with him, but she insisted on maintaining her own home.

Throughout the busy days Albrecht was aware of an emptiness that haunted him. When at last he found himself alone in his workshop, he allowed himself to mourn. He took refuge in reading the Bible that his father had so often discussed with him. He thought of his father speaking of the joy of everlasting salvation, and he wrote in his diary:

"This man, my dear father, was very careful of his children to bring them up to honor God. For it was his highest wish to train them well, that they might be pleasing in the sight of both God and man. Wherefore his daily speech to us was that we should love God and deal truly with our neighbors...God is full of compassion; through which may He grant us after this pitiful life the joy of everlasting salvation—in the name of the Father, the Son and the Holy Ghost, at the beginning and at the end, one eternal Governour. Amen."

Albrecht buried himself in hard work and further studies for his paintings. He produced more woodcut designs, completed commissions for paintings, and pursued a study of human proportions.

One morning while the dew was still wet on the grass, he went outside the city wall and dug a piece of turf which he brought back to his workshop. Albrecht wanted to study the smallest details of creation so that he might learn as his former teacher Herr Wolgemut used to say, "from God, the Great Art Master."

Albrecht carefully painted every blade of grass. There were dandelions tightly closed and the fleshy leaves of the great plantain. He painted the creeping Charlie, the cock's foot and the heath rush with its thin spikes.

Agnes spied his newest painting and cocked her head to one side, her braid swinging jauntily down her back. "It is so real I think I could touch it!" she exclaimed. "But who will buy a portrait of grass?"

"This one is for me," replied Albrecht. "I am taking a lesson from creation today."

Albrecht used his studies for a watercolor that he called "The Virgin with a Multitude of Animals." His idea was for all of nature to give thanks for the birth of Christ. He not only placed the traditional shepherds in the background, but he filled the composition with a variety of animals and plants. He even painted his faithful dog Franz at the feet of Mary.

Two years after his father's death, his mother consented to come and live with Albrecht and Agnes. The Dürer workshop had grown during the past few years. Albrecht had taken on more apprentices and a journeyman. Albrecht's mother decided that she was needed to help Agnes market Albrecht's artwork. "I helped your father for many years," she announced. "I can be a great help to Agnes now."

Albrecht's mother visited the workshop early one morning. She found her son already at work on a drawing of Adam and Eve.

"I designed this to illustrate them before they sinned," said Albrecht. "God created Adam and Eve sinless, and I want to show this by drawing them as perfect in beauty as I am able."

"Your father always said that beauty was a difficult thing to capture."

"He spoke truly," replied Albrecht with a sigh. "I still have more to learn. I have been thinking of a plan, but I would need your help."

Albrecht's mother listened as he unfolded his idea to return to Venice. "Merchants from all over the world are there, and I could make as much in a year in Venice as I could earn in five years in Nurnberg. I could also meet the best Italian artists and bring their skills back to Nurnberg."

His mother looked doubtful. "Who would organize the sales at the fairs?"

Albrecht took a deep breath and launched his proposal. "I have been talking with Agnes and she thinks she can market the prints and books at fairs if you will help."

Albrecht's mother was silent for a few moments as she calculated the work in her head. At last she said, "I think it could be done. You will have to send money home by the Imhoff baggage train, but I think we can do a considerable amount to make ends meet."

Chapter 11

"For, verily, art is embedded in nature; he who can extract it has it."

Albrecht Dürer

Paint Brushes

Albrecht joined the throng of people in Saint Mark's Square in Venice. Though the square was crowded he found a place to stand near the Ducal Palace. He drew a quick sketch of the palace. Its rows of thin pillars and delicate pinnacles resembled lace.

Albrecht wished his brother Hans could have seen this place. He had tried to convince his mother to let Hans join him, but she said she was afraid "the sky would fall in on him!" Albrecht had protested that Hans would be lost among the women, but his mother was adamant.

The sound of a choir marked the beginning of the Procession of the Cross. Albrecht carefully folded his sketch and watched as clergymen and city leaders marched the circumference of the square.

Four holy men in white robes carried a piece of the cross in a beautifully decorated box. Four more men carried an ornate canopy over the box. The procession moved slowly, and Albrecht turned his attention to St. Mark's Basilica, which lay next to the Ducal Palace.

The sun sparkled on the magnificent facade of the Basilica.

Albrecht admired the columns of precious marble, the arches decorated in gold, and the intricate mosaics which told the story of how the body of St. Mark came to Venice. Above the main entrance the statues of four horses gleamed.

Albrecht edged around the sides of the crowd in order to get a better view of the horses. He had an idea to study the proportions of horses from a mathematical point of view. "The sculptor of these horses was truly an artist," he murmured.

"What, an artist?" asked a shrill voice at his elbow.

Albrecht turned to see an elderly women. She was stooped with age and further bent by a load of fruit she carried in a basket. "I was admiring the horses on the basilica," replied Albrecht.

"And I can see by the look of you that you be an artist," replied the women. "There are too many of them in Venice to suit me. Still, they make some nice things."

Albrecht had a sudden idea. "You would make an excellent subject for a drawing. Would you permit me to make your drawing?"

The woman looked at Albrecht suspiciously. "Why would you draw a crooked old woman?"

"Let me show you," replied Albrecht even as he pulled out his paper and charcoal. The woman clutched her fruit basket with a mixture of suspense and awe. When Albrecht showed her the completed sketch she gasped. "It is the very likeness!"

"I could use this in a painting I will make from the Bible," said Albrecht. He began to put the sketch into his jacket pocket, but when he noticed the wistful expression on the woman's face he offered it to her.

She clutched the gift, almost spilling her basket of fruit. "My son will be so proud," she cried. "A real portrait like the grand ladies have."

Back in his lodging, Albrecht made a second portrait of the old woman from memory. He thought it would come in useful.

During his stay in Venice, Albrecht renewed acquaintances with old friends and made new friends as well. One of his new acquaintances was the famous artist, Gentile Bellini. Though he was much older than Albrecht, he had lost none of his vigor and enthusiasm for art. He invited Albrecht to visit him in his studio.

The studio of the Great Bellini was located on a narrow back alley. From the exterior the building appeared to be just another narrow town house squeezed between similar homes, but once through the door, Albrecht found himself in an amazing work shop.

Sun streamed through several large windows that held views of a canal. Rich tapestries adorned a center area that was set like a stage. Amid lush palm trees three Turkish men, wearing large turbans, stood in profile. Their ornate costumes held Albrecht's eyes for a moment.

"*Magnifico!*" called a small man who was painting nearby. He stood at a large canvas that glowed with beautiful colors. "It will be a magnificent painting of the wise men with the infant Jesus..." He stopped abruptly when he saw Albrecht and warmly extended his arms for an embrace.

"Thank you for the invitation to your workshop," Albrecht said, feeling awkward amidst the grand surroundings. "I already owe you more than I can repay for your lessons on the art of perspective."

The artist flung his hands in the air. "It is nothing, my dear friend. I brought you here today to see my new models. They are *magnifico*, no?"

"I have never seen any to compare," replied Albrecht.

"You make a sketch for your portfolio," offered Bellini. "You will use it one day."

"I couldn't..." Albrecht began to protest, but Bellini pushed the drawing materials into his hands.

"You and I are master painters. We understand each other. Please make your sketch."

Albrecht realized that his remonstrance was useless in the face of his friend's hospitality. He thanked the artist and took a place near the back of the room. As Albrecht studied the three men intently, his hands worked swiftly and surely. He drew every detail of the men's' costumes into his drawing. He concentrated so intently that he was unaware of the movement of Bellini's assistants around him, or even of the work of Bellini himself.

The sound of two sharp claps brought Albrecht out of his study.

"It is time for the repast," announced Bellini. An assistant led the Turkish men through a side door and Albrecht finished a last detail before they disappeared.

Bellini beckoned to Albrecht. "You liked the sketching?" he asked.

"Yes, the details were excellent. Where did you find them?"

"Venice has men from many countries who come here to trade. I simply asked my assistant to search the port for me."

The two men enjoyed a leisurely Italian meal. Bellini was profuse in his praise of Albrecht's work. He asked if he might have a drawing of Albrecht's as a memento. Albrecht laughed and promised that he would give him a drawing if Bellini would return the favor.

As Bellini led Albrecht back to his studio, his face grew serious. "Will you be so kind, Albrecht, as to gratify a friend in a small matter?"

"Please ask of me anything I can do for you," replied Albrecht.

Bellini opened the door to his well-stocked studio and waited for his friend to enter. He hesitated a moment before he said, "I want you to make me a present of one of the brushes with which you paint hairs."

Albrecht was surprised by the simple request. He brought out several of the brushes he had with him. "Choose those you like best or take them all if you like."

The older artist peered at the offered brushes. It was his turn to be surprised. "No, I don't mean these but the ones you use to paint several hairs with one stroke. They must be rather spread out and more divided, no? You make a long sweep, and the distance between hairs remains the same."

"These are the brushes I use," said Albrecht. He feared that he was upsetting his friend. "Look, I will show you." He took one of the brushes and carefully painted long wavy tresses, such as a woman might wear. Each individual hair stood out in the most regular order and symmetry.

Bellini looked on wondering. "No human being could have convinced me by report of the truth that I see with my own eyes!" He embraced Albrecht with his characteristic vigor. "Thank you my friend. I have many brushes like this one, but I would like to keep one of your brushes all the same."

Chapter 12

"The Creator fashioned men once for all as they must be, and I hold that the perfection of form and beauty is contained in the sum of all men."
Albrecht Dürer

Home Again

During his stay in Venice Albrecht kept up a faithful correspondence with Willibald. They confided in each other when they met with success: in politics in the case of Willibald, and in art in Albrecht's case.

Albrecht wrote to tell Willibald of a painting he had made in only five days. It was an interesting study called "Christ Among the Doctors" and it showed only hands and faces. The doctors' gnarled hands and wrinkled faces formed a sharp contrast to the face of the young Jesus. Albrecht also confided in Willibald the threat of poisoning he faced from jealous painters.

Willibald had risen politically until he was a member of the City Council of Nurnberg. Albrecht was proud of his friend but could not resist the temptation to tease him. In one letter he wrote:

Your letter telling me of the praise you get to overflowing from the princes and nobles gave me great delight. You must have completely reversed yourself to have become so gentle: I'll hardly know you when I come home.

In another letter he wrote:

How good we feel, both of us, I with my picture and you cum voster wisdom. When we are praised we turn up our noses and believe it all. But there might stand a nasty mocker behind us and scoff at us.

During his year in Venice Albrecht received disturbing news from Agnes. His cousin Niklas often traveled selling golden wares. During one of his trips he was kidnapped by the henchmen of the infamous Graf Asmus von Wertheim. At the time Niklas was carrying five thousand florins' worth of gems!

Albrecht shuddered at the thought of his cousin in the hands of these unscrupulous men. Stories were told of how they tortured their victims to extract higher ransoms.

Albrecht knew that Niklas could not raise a large ransom. Even if he survived, he would be impoverished for the rest of his life. Agnes soon wrote that Niklas had been ransomed by the Nurnberg City Council. Albrecht wondered how Niklas would support his young family after reimbursing the City Council.

The months in Italy passed quickly. Albrecht completed enough works to establish his reputation as a painter and provide a handsome income for his family. His greatest work was the Rose Garden Altar which he painted for a group of German merchants living in Venice. He also studied the new science of perspective which was only known in Italy at that time. He bought a copy of a geometry book by Euclid. He would have much material for future study.

Shortly before he left for home, he rode to Bologna to learn more of the secret art of perspective from a man who was willing to teach him. Was the man Leonardo da Vinci? Even to this day, it remains a secret. At last he traveled home soon after Christmas 1506.

The coachman cracked his whip and urged the horses to greater speed. The forest was not a place to tarry. Though the laws and courts of Nurnberg extended to these regions, they were in no way a promise of safe travel.

Inside the coach, Albrecht sketched the fascinating tangle of undergrowth that grew close to the road. Despite the rutted road which jolted the coach, his hand was steady. As he drew, he thought of how good it would be to return home.

Albrecht had ambitious plans to develop his studio. He would take apprentices and teach them the secrets of art and perspective that he had learned in Italy. He would enrich the art of his beloved country by writing a textbook for artists. Albrecht glanced through a growing folder of notes for his textbook. He would begin with instruction on the way an artist should be raised.

He added another note to his outline:

The young apprentice is to be brought up in the fear of God and taught to pray to God for the grace of quick perception and to honor God. He must also be pure, for nothing so blunts the understanding as immorality.

The sudden brightness of sunlight made Albrecht look up from his notes. The carriage had left the forest for the broad fields surrounding Nurnberg. In the far distance stood the city rising on its hill. Albrecht looked fondly at the stone walls and steeples of his home. Above them all the Citadel stood squarely on the brow of the hill. No other skyline could compare to Nurnberg, Albrecht thought with satisfaction. Even the glittering Venice seemed shallow and transparent by comparison.

At last the coach clattered through the thick archway of the city walls. As the horses pulled up to the Dürer home, Albrecht sprang from the coach before it had even stopped. He found Agnes working at her books in the front room. Her look of surprise and delight at seeing him melted the weariness of his travels. He wrapped her in a warm hug.

"How have you been, *mein* Agnes?"

"I am glad you are home at last," she replied. Albrecht thought there were tears in her eyes, but Agnes brushed past him to see to the coachman and direct his luggage to be unloaded.

The next few months were busy, happy months for the Dürers. Albrecht and Agnes had much to discuss. Albrecht immediately began to develop his portfolio of ideas. While in Venice, he had experimented with increasing the density of shadows to show more atmosphere. He incorporated these ideas into two series of woodcuts which he had started before his trip.

These woodcuts showed the Passion of Christ, and gave Albrecht time to think about certain Bible passages. Agnes had

Christ on the mount of Olives

grown even more devout during his absence. She eagerly discussed the woodcuts with him, and Albrecht showed her how he illustrated various parts of the Bible account.

Albrecht also painted "The Martyrdom of the Ten Thousand Christians" as an altarpiece for Elector Frederick of Saxony, and another altarpiece for a successful businessman named Herr Heller. The paintings required almost all of his daylight hours as well as the contributions of his apprentices. Albrecht's brother Hans had worked for Herr Wolgemut during his absence. He was a skilled artist in his own right. He did much of the work on the side panels of the Heller altarpiece.

Albrecht set high standards for his paintings. He insisted that the colors be laid on several layers thick so that the painting would last for hundreds of years. This took a considerable amount of time and expense, since the pigments for the paint were costly.

Albrecht also spent time instructing his apprentices. Like his own teacher, Herr Wolgemut, he required his students to study art from real life. One of his youngest apprentices was named Hans Baldung. He was a lanky youth with tousled brown hair and penetrating brown eyes. One afternoon Albrecht gave a lesson on perspective and assigned his students to draw a landscape.

"But I want to do the truly great art, like a Madonna or a religious theme," Hans protested.

Albrecht turned from a painting where he was applying the delicate grain of velvet to a robe. "Hans, every blade of grass, each gentle creature is created by God and is therefore a religious theme. I am giving you the greatest themes of all so that you can improve your skill."

Hans' face fell. "I am impatient to be able to draw well now..."

Albrecht laid aside his brush and sat beside the boy. "The understanding must begin to grow side by side with skill, so that the hand has power to do what the will commands. Your skill will grow with time, but you must allow your understanding, like the things I am teaching you about perspective, to mature as well. These two must mature together, for the one is nothing without the other."

Christ Among the Doctors

"There is nothing good in us except it becomes good in Christ. Whosoever therefore will altogether justify himself is unjust. If we will what is good, Christ wills it in us. No human repentance is enough to equalize deadly sin and be fruitful."
Albrecht Dürer

New Friends

The new Dürer home sat squarely on the end of the street which led to the Tiergartner Gate, one of the main gates into the city. The house was built of sandstone and half-timbered. It had once belonged to an astronomer who kept a spacious study on the second floor where a large window admitted the western sun. On the main floor the thick glass of bulls-eye windows lit the kitchen and living area.

When Albrecht first brought Agnes to their new home, she threw open the bull-eye windows and caught her breath at the magnificent view of the Citadel which rose above them. She looked approvingly over the dark paneling in the main room and the kitchen with its broad chimney. "It is a good house," she pronounced. "And a good neighborhood."

Agnes was happy in her new home, but Albrecht often caught her looking wistfully at the other young women in the neighborhood who had children of their own. He tried to comfort her. "Though God has not given us children of our own, he has given us a large responsibility for the boys who come to us as apprentices," he told her.

Agnes knew he was right. Several of the boys lived with them, and she treated them like sons. She saw to it that they were properly fed and insisted that all the apprentices have an extra allowance to pay for weekly baths at the public bath house.

As the Dürer workshop grew in wealth, Agnes brought an idea to Albrecht. "Could we put aside money for the education of craftsmen's sons who could not afford to go to school?" she asked. Albrecht thought it was an excellent idea. He entrusted Agnes, with her keen business sense, to develop a scholarship fund.

A few houses down the street from the Dürers was the House of the Unicorn. It was owned by Lazarus Spengler, the accomplished secretary to the Nurnberg Council. Like Albrecht he came from a large family. He was the ninth of twenty-one children.

Willibald introduced the two men. Albrecht learned that Lazarus had studied law, but, like Willibald, he had deliberately left the university before he was given the law degree since lawyers were not allowed on the council. Lazarus was recognized as one of the most valuable consultants in the area of law and was often sent on delegations to negotiate rights and treaties for the city of Nurnberg.

The men became good friends. They both attended meetings of the new "School for Poets" founded by the court poet, Conrad Celtis. Celtis had started a revival of poetry in the city.

Lazarus had a quick wit to match his quick mind. Soon Albrecht and he were exchanging poetry. Albrecht wrote several proverbs in verse:

Who seeks for dirt will want no more,
If first he sweeps before his door.

Each thinks he knows all men below,
Though himself he does not know.

Who of his tongue is not the master,
Never speaks without disaster.

He also wrote a set of verses about good and bad friends:

Who turns away from his friend in need,
He is not a true friend in deed.
Who always will be in the right,

With him it is no use to fight.
He who is truly thy good friend
Will use no cunning for his end.
He'll turn thee back from evil ways,
And guide thee rightly all thy days.

Albrecht had truly found a set of good friends. He had many opportunities to meet with Willibald, Lazarus Spengler and others. They gave him the opportunity to discuss fresh ideas. They also shared a common link with Albrecht since they had traveled and studied outside of Nurnberg. Their broader view of knowledge and art fascinated and challenged Albrecht.

The center of their meetings soon became Willibald's home. As Albrecht and Willibald had talked of Roman mythology as boys, they now talked of Roman philosophy and artifacts. They also began to discuss another ancient topic: the Christian faith.

On a cool evening in June, Albrecht walked to the Pirckheimer home, which lay on the west side of the Market Square. He passed the Church of Our Lady with its clock that showed the phases of the moon and paused to admire Nurnberg's "Beautiful Fountain," which stood in the center of the open square. Ancient heroes adorned the fountain, with Moses and the prophets at the top, and such famous men as the warrior Joshua, King David, Alexander the Great, Julius Caesar, and Charlemagne around the sides. The statues seemed to beckon from their perches, as though calling passersby to continue to fight for the good.

When Albrecht arrived, Willibald cheerfully waved him into his study.

"Here is a letter from a friend from Italy. He sends greetings to you and says that your print of the Prodigal Son is admired everywhere."

"I am surprised that it suits the luxurious Italian tastes," replied Albrecht.

"But that is what my friend admires. You tell the story in a fresh way. Most artists paint the prodigal during his sinful days, but you captured his moment of repentance!"

Willibald shuffled rapidly through the papers on his desk. "Here is something else that I want you to read." He held out a sheaf of notes. "I have been reading some of the early church fathers, and I have made a short translation of the Orations of Gregory Nazianzen for you."

The Prodigal Son amoung the Swine

Albrecht read the papers carefully. "It appears that the Church has changed its views since the days of the early church fathers. If I am not mistaken, these writings agree with the Bible."

"Precisely!" said Willibald, his eyes sparkling. "Those who are educated in such things must study and reveal the truth of the Scriptures to the rest of the world."

As he was talking, a maid showed Lazarus Spengler into the room.

"And how does one tell the rest of the world?" Lazarus interrupted.

Willibald chuckled. "I have a plan, but first let us have dinner."

The dinner was a sumptuous meal of chicken with fish in a ginger sauce, followed by sweet cakes filled with minced pork. Willibald insisted on leaving the serious talk until after dinner, but the three men soon found themselves in a spirited debate on the topic of art. Albrecht had begun the discussion when he put forth his idea that true beauty was hidden in nature.

Lazarus was intrigued with the idea. "Are you saying that certain objects are beautiful naturally? For example, will all pictures of babies be beautiful?"

Albrecht hastened to explain his comment. "Not necessarily. There is a difference between the beauty of an object represented in a work of art and the beauty of the work of art itself. A great artist can show the beauty that is hidden even in rustic things."

"How are we to determine beauty? Human judgment or common taste?" asked Lazarus. He neatly cut an apple in two and began to slice it in sections.

Albrecht helped himself to a section of apple. "Neither," he said forcefully.

"Then how can you ever know what beauty is?" challenged Willibald.

Albrecht stroked his beard and sat back in his chair to enjoy the discussion better. "I don't think that any man lives who can grasp the whole beauty of the meanest living creature, and certainly not of a man since he is an extraordinary creation of God and master of the other creatures."

Willibald almost choked on his food. "Wait! Do you grant that one man will conceive and make a more beautiful figure and will explain the natural cause of its beauty more reasonably than another?"

"Yes, but not to such an extent that there could not be anything more beautiful. Man cannot conceive so fair a thing. God alone knows such. He reveals a small understanding of beauty to some people."

"So you are saying that true beauty can only come from God?" asked Lazarus.

"I am saying that only God knows the true beauty."

Willibald reached for another sweet cake. "What you say makes sense, but if only God knows the true beauty, then why do you work so hard at instructing others in art?"

Albrecht leaned forward. His tone was more intense as he answered. "Though we are in such a state of error, I am glad to help as much as I can, so that the gross deformities of our work might be pruned away and avoided."

Lazarus finished the last piece of fruit and delicately placed his napkin on the table. "Albrecht, shouldn't we rather wholly cease from learning if we cannot attain perfection?"

"By no means!" All pretense of languor vanished. "Evil and good lie before men, and it behooves a rational man to choose the good. We should earnestly seek to learn the criteria of that beauty which can be known to men."

Willibald watched his friend's outburst with amusement. "There are some subjects that Albrecht cannot discuss with detachment. Gentlemen, I too have a subject that is close to my heart."

Beginning with a description of some sermons he had read, Willibald unfolded to the friends a plan to form a club to study the Bible. "I am specifically interested in some sermons that I have read from the Augustinian monks. I want to invite one of them to speak in our community."

Albrecht noted a tone of triumph in his friend's voice as he made the last announcement.

"Do you think they will come?" asked Lazarus.

"Nurnberg is an important city that needs to hear the kind of sermons these men preach," replied Willibald. "They will come."

That night Albrecht could not sleep. The men had talked of the Bible long into the night, and his thoughts kept returning to their discussion. At last he lit a candle and without waking Agnes, made his way to his desk. He found a piece of paper and his pen and began to write:

Thus says Albrecht Dürer the painter, who marks his engravings with the monogram A D.

Every soul which attains everlasting life is quickened in Christ Jesus, who is both God and Man, two substances in one person, which can only be believed by Faith and never understood by the human Reason.

At last, satisfied that he had recorded his thoughts, he extinguished his candle and made his way back to bed.

Chapter 14

*"For he has repented of and made atonement for the sins
of the whole world, and has obtained of the Father
Everlasting Life. Therefore Christ Jesus is the Son of God,
the highest power, who can do all things, and He is the
Eternal Life."*
Albrecht Dürer

Apelles and the Cobbler

A gnes sat straight in her chair and listened intently as
Albrecht read his poem.

"This is the first rhyme I made," he explained. "And this is
what I wrote:

*Thou mirror of all Angels and Redeemer of mankind,
A ransom for my sin let me in Thy martyrdom find.*

"That is wonderful!" exclaimed Agnes. "I did not know that you
could write such poetry."

Albrecht smiled sheepishly. "I thought I had succeeded well
because each line had the same number of syllables."

"Then why did Willibald laugh at them?" asked Agnes, her
blue eyes filled with indignation.

"He said no rhyme ought to have more than eight syllables."

"Hmm." Agnes did not try to hide her suspicion of such
nonsense. "It is an honest rhyme on a true theme, which is more
than I can say for some of Willibald's works."

"I'm not the expert on such things, but I decided to begin again
and make a new rhyme. Each line has eight syllables." Albrecht
drew a deep breath. "Here it is:

Strive earnestly with all thy might,
That God should give thee Wisdom's light.
He doth his wisdom truly prove,
Whom neither dearth nor riches move.
And he shall also be called wise,
Who joy and sorrow both defies.
He who bears both honour and shame,
He well deserves the wise man's name.
Who knows himself and evil shuns,
In Wisdom's path he surely runs.
Who 'gainst his foe doth vengeance cherish,
In hell-flame doth his wisdom perish.
Who strives against the devil's might,
The Lord will help him in the fight.
Who keeps his heart for ever pure,
He of Wisdom's crown is sure.
And who loves God with all his heart,
Chooses the wise and better part.

Agnes clapped her hands as he completed his poem. "That is even better than the first! Surely, Willibald admitted it."

Albrecht shook his head. "He did not like it."

"That is preposterous! You must take your poem to Lazarus Spengler. He will give you a fair judgment."

Albrecht tried not to laugh as he saw his wife's concern. He allowed himself to be muffled in his best cloak, and soon found himself knocking at the door of the House of the Unicorn.

Lazarus' sister-in-law answered the door. She was a refined and generous woman, who was raising Lazarus' children since his wife was an invalid.

"How is your mother?" she asked politely.

"She continues to fare poorly," Albrecht answered.

"Then I will prepare some of my special soup for her while you talk with my brother."

Lazarus gladly listened to Albrecht's story of the two poems. "Willibald is too confident," he said. "Your poetry is as good as the next man's at the Poet's School."

"But I want to be better," replied Albrecht. "Will you help me put my meaning into rhymes?"

Lazarus immediately sharpened the point of his pen and set to work. By the end of the evening a new poem had been set forth to the satisfaction of both men, and Albrecht returned home with a pot of soup for his mother.

Agnes greeted him at the door and wanted to hear how the poem fared.

"We will see what Willibald thinks of the new poem," said Albrecht, "but I think he will have to admit that it is good!"

Albrecht's work kept him so busy that weeks passed before he thought of the poem again. He had recently become a member of the Great Council which met to discuss laws and concerns in Nurnberg. At the same time he had several commissions and a busy workshop to manage. He was experimenting with copper engraving, the technique he had developed with Herr Wolgemut.

Albrecht found that copper engraving was especially suited to increasing the depth of feeling portrayed in a picture. While wood blocks were carved so that the raised area could be inked, copper plates were etched with a burin so that ink would fill the grooves. Ink was applied with a cloth and the surface was wiped clean. Only the ink in the grooves remained. The paper picked up the ink design when it was squeezed through the rollers of a press. Albrecht used the unique effects of the burin on a soft copper plate to create breathtaking fidelity. His goal was to mirror life as exactly as possible.

Albrecht was also working on an altarpiece which he called "The Trinity Adored by All the Saints." It was for the chapel of an almshouse dedicated to the saints. Albrecht wanted to show how all believers in all times were part of the community of faith.

He pictured a symbol of the Trinity in the sky surrounded by cherubim and saints, including a Nurnberg girl, a king, a monk, a knight, a farmer and a laborer. He even put himself in the painting!

As he painted he instructed his apprentices. He read them parts of the textbook he was preparing for young artists. One session he began with one of his texts.

Albrecht read: "No one should allow himself to be deterred from this study because he does not at once understand the whole, for what is quite easy can be no very high art, but what is full of art calls for diligence, pains, and labor, before it can be understood and fixed in the memory."

Albrecht paused. He saw that the youngest apprentice, Hans Baldung, was listening carefully. "This is the reason I require such serious study from nature. You are learning when you draw from creation."

Albrecht reflected how Hans had certainly improved during the hours he had spent in practice. Hans raised his hand and Albrecht acknowledged him.

"What if I think there is a better way to draw people than what we find in nature?"

Albrecht thought carefully before he answered. "I would rather have you choose the best parts from many to be united in one figure, than create your own ideal. The more nearly and accurately a figure is made to resemble a man, so much the better will the work be. The Creator fashioned men once for all as they must be, and I hold that the perfection of form and beauty is contained in the sum of all men. I would not follow an artist who invents some new body of proportions which is not found among men."

He finished his lecture by taking the recent work of each apprentice in turn and showing the parts that were good and the parts which needed improvement. "Work well-done is honoring to God," he concluded. "Continue to use your gifts well."

That week Albrecht received a poem from Lazarus which was Willibald's response to Albrecht's poetry. It was a satirical poem that told the story of the famous Greek artist, Apelles, and a cobbler. In the end the cobbler is told to stick to his craft because he will never become a good artist.

Willibald was really making fun of Albrecht becoming a poet, but it was so cleverly written that Albrecht laughed when he read it. It inspired him to draw a cartoon for his friend Lazarus.

At the top of the cartoon he wrote, "Dear Lazarus Spengler, I am sending you herewith the cake which for lack of leisure I could not bake before. Enjoy it!"

In the picture three men worked furiously at their jobs. The caption read, "Superb missives are here cast, printed and baked in the year 1511." The fanciful cartoon portrayed Lazarus and two of their friends as though they were mindlessly churning out legal documents in a bakery. All of the friends enjoyed the joke. For Willibald, Albrecht decided to write another poem.

When he read his responding poem to Agnes, she laughed until the tears ran down her cheeks. She insisted that Albrecht make her a copy. She kept it with her papers and liked to take it out and read it from time to time.

In Nurnberg it is known full well
A man of letter now doth dwell,
...And he has made a jest of me,
Because I made some poetry,
And of True Wisdom something wrote.
But as he likes my verses not,
He makes a laughing stock of me,
And says I'm like the Cobbler, he
Who criticized Apelles' art.
With this he tries to make me smart,
Because he thinks it is for me
To paint, and not write poetry.
But I have undertaken this
(And will not stop for him or his),
To learn whatever thing I can
For which will blame me no wise man.
For he who only learns one thing,
And to naught else his mind doth bring,
To him as to the notary,
It haps, who lived here as do we,
In this our town. To him was known
To write one form and one alone.
Two men came to him with a need
That he should draw them up a deed;
And he proceeded very well,
Until their names he came to spell:

Gotz was the first name that perplexed,
And Rosenstammen was the next.
The notary was much astonished,
And thus his clients he admonished,
'Dear friends,' he said, 'you must be wrong,
These names don't to my form belong.
Franz and Fritz I know full well,
But of no others have heard tell.'
And so he drove away his clients,
And people mocked his little science.
To me that it may hap not so,
Something of all things I will know....
Therefore I will still make rhymes,
Though my friend may laugh at times.
So the Painter with hairy beard
Says to the Writer who mocked and jeered.

Rinocerous

"All worldly rulers in these dangerous times should give good heed that they receive not human misguidance for the Word of God, for God will have nothing added to His Word nor taken away from it."

Albrecht Dürer

Sodalitas Martiniana

The painter with the hairy beard was becoming a renowned artist. His prints were sold all over the world, and he received commissions for paintings from the most wealthy and influential men of his day. In 1512, the Emperor Maximilian, himself, commissioned the first of many works of art which would follow over the years.

Despite his fame, Albrecht never grew weary of learning new things. He read the ancient works as they were translated. He discussed new ideas with his group of friends. He even sought to learn about unusual events.

When a rare animal called a rhinoceros went on display in Lisbon, Albrecht requested a full description of it from a friend who lived there. He made a print of the creature which became very popular.

On May 17, 1514, one of the saddest events of his life occurred. His mother died after a long illness. Before she died she wished Albrecht peace with God and exhorted him to keep himself from sin. She struggled painfully as she died, and Albrecht asked her if she were afraid.

"I am afraid of death," she replied. "But I am not afraid to come before God."

A portrait of Albrecht's mother in old age

Albrecht mourned for his mother and wrote, "To speak of God was ever her greatest delight and gladly she beheld the honour of God."

Albrecht turned his grief into art as he buried himself in work. He produced some of his most enduring works during this time, including "The Knight, Death and the Devil," "St. Jerome in his Study," and "Melancolia. I."

Willibald was true to his word, and the Vicar-General of the German Congregation of Augustinians came to Nurnberg. His name was Father Staupitz and he was the former dean of the Theological Faculty at the University of Wittenberg. He delivered the Advent and Christmas sermons on the theme: On True Repentance.

Albrecht was impressed with the powerful and clear sermons. Staupitz explained that man was fallen and that it was by divine grace he could be saved. He stressed that God is infinite in His capacity to forgive sins. From the Bible he carefully showed that Christ's death, and not empty ceremony, was the only way to salvation.

Albrecht and his friends began to call themselves "the Sodalitas Staupitziana" which meant "the soldiers of Staupitz." They met to discuss the Bible and the growing number of tracts that were appearing.

The next year a prior of the Augustinian Monastery in Wittenberg came to give the Lenten and Easter sermons. His name was Dr. Wenceslas Linck, and his sermons were so reasonable and forceful that many more people became earnest in studying the Bible.

A few months later another Augustinian by the name of Martin Luther nailed *Ninety-five Theses* to the door of the Wittenberg Castle. The theses were meant to expose errors which had infiltrated the church. There were errors like allowing people to pay money to buy loved ones out of Purgatory.

Martin Luther asserted that salvation is by grace alone, and could not be bought. He had not meant for the theses to be widely circulated, but two days later a copy found its way into the hands of Albrecht's group of friends. One of the men, named Kaspar Nutzel, immediately prepared a German translation.

Albrecht was one of the first people in Germany to read the document. He so admired the doctrines laid forth, that he sent a gift to Martin Luther and expressed his thanks. A correspondence began between the two men.

One evening Albrecht was meeting with his friends at Willibald's home. Willibald was blustering about a topic for which he was rapidly running out of facts.

"Your reasoning is going in a circle," said Albrecht.

"But what you say cannot be painted!" replied Willibald.

"Nay, but what you advance cannot be put into words or even figured to the mind."

As the men laughed at Albrecht's witty retort, there was a loud knocking at the door. Willibald looked around the group with an air of mystery. "Gentleman, I would like to introduce to you a promising young man who is traveling to his new position at the Wittenberg University. I had hoped he would arrive this evening."

The maid opened the door and showed in a young man. He was thin, with angular features, but what Albrecht noticed were his eyes, which were large and gentle.

"This is Philip Melanchthon," said Willibald.

Albrecht liked the young professor at once. Like Albrecht, he had come to admire the writings of Martin Luther. The two men talked for several hours about God and faith.

The next year the Diet of Augsburg was held. Diets were meetings held to discuss the weighty issues of the empire. Many important people such as Elector Frederick of Saxony would be there, and the Nurnberg delegation decided to invite Albrecht so that he could draw portraits. Albrecht was thrilled. He knew that the works of Martin Luther were to be discussed at the diet.

Albrecht accompanied Lazarus Spengler, Kaspar Nutzel, and Leonhard Groland. All of the men were thoroughly convinced of the Biblical truths taught by Martin Luther.

A portrait of Melanchthon

On their journey Albrecht brought out two tracts by Luther. "Gentlemen, these booklets are beautifully written. They are ordered in a logical way and are faithful to the Scriptures. After reading three or four paragraphs I could grasp the problem to be worked out in the whole booklet!"

Lazarus smiled. "That is high praise since I have read through other books in their entirety and still not understood what the author was trying to convey."

"Exactly! That is why I consider this Martin Luther to be such a valuable man for the Christian faith. At the diet I propose that we do all we can to support him."

Lazarus agreed. "I hold you all to secrecy when I tell you that I am writing a defense of Luther which I will publish anonymously."

Albrecht had read Lazarus' writings. They were scholarly and well-written. Lazarus had translated Eusebius' *Life and Death of Saint Jerome* and had written *Admonition and Instruction for a Virtuous Life* in rhyme. In the second book he used classical quotations and Bible verses. He dedicated it to Albrecht, "his special, intimate and brotherly friend."

"If your defense of Luther is like your other books, it will be received well," Albrecht assured him.

During the diet the men once again saw Father Staupitz who had first preached the Bible to them in Nurnberg. Staupitz greeted them warmly, but bore a heavy burden. "I will be releasing Martin Luther from his vows," he explained to Albrecht and the Nurnberg delegation.

Albrecht gasped in surprise. "Why will he be released?"

"He says he cannot serve God as an Augustinian any longer."

Albrecht pondered his words. Did that mean that he and his friends would have to leave the church also?

Lazarus was thoughtful after their conversation. "I fear the results of the little defense I am writing for Luther," he told Albrecht.

Albrecht nodded slowly. "We will have to choose whether we stand with Martin Luther or not."

Back home in Nurnberg the group of men changed their name from "Sodalitas Staupitziana" to "Sodalitas Martiniana." Soldiers of Martin.

Albrecht had an increasing amount of work for Emperor Maximilian. The emperor, though lacking in the wealth of former rulers, had a grand view of his position. He saw himself as one of a long line of knights and warrior kings. Albrecht painted two portraits of the emperor in which he portrayed him as a knight-errant. As a companion to one of the portraits, he painted Charlemagne, the greatest warrior king of the German nation.

Albrecht was also commissioned to direct the work on a series of woodcuts of the triumphal procession which would measure sixty-five yards in length. Since the emperor could not afford to construct a real triumphal arch in stone, he would have one built of paper. Each square of paper would have an original woodcut print that illustrated his reign or a related topic.

Albrecht also illustrated the margins of forty-five pages of a printed prayer book for the Emperor. For all his service, Albrecht received a pension from the Emperor.

Albrecht had an increasing correspondence with influential men whom he had met at the diet or through letters. One new acquaintance was Spalatin, the chaplain of Elector Frederick of Saxony. Spalatin sent Albrecht one of Luther's books. Albrecht wrote to the chaplain:

I pray your worthiness to beseech his Electoral Grace to take the praiseworthy Doctor Martin Luther under his protection, for the sake of Christian truth, for that is of more importance to us than all the power and riches of this world; because all things pass away with time; truth alone endureth for ever. God helping me, if ever I meet Dr. Martin Luther, I intend to draw his portrait carefully from life and engrave it on copper, to be a lasting remembrance of a Christian man, who helped me out of great distress. And I beg your worthiness to send me for my money anything new that Doctor Martin may write.

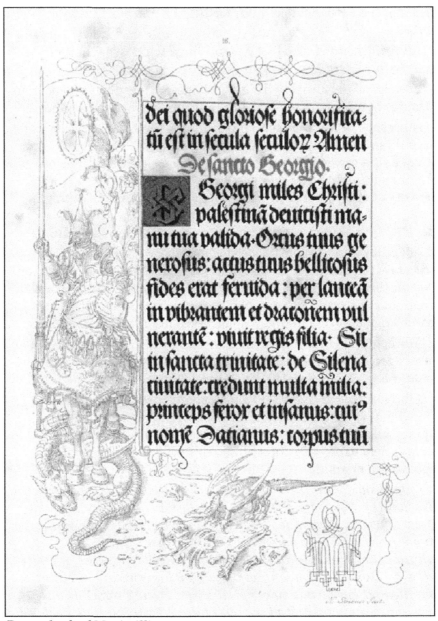

Prayer book of Maximillian

Chapter 16

*"Reality is not a bewildering mass of ideas, but is ordered,
and this order can be discovered by experience."*
Albrecht Dürer

A Cloud of Worry

It was a soft gray evening, and the first stars were coming out as Albrecht sat at a desk in Willibald's home. Willibald had asked him to illustrate some of the cover pages of precious books in his library. Albrecht skillfully drew scrolls and coats of arms while he listened to the other men talk.

"Dr. Eck is a disgrace to his profession!" blustered Willibald. "How can he call himself a church man and professor when he denies that Christ's death purchased our salvation?"

As Albrecht drew, he thought of the news he had heard of Dr. Eck. He was a professor from Ingolstadt who had challenged Martin Luther to a debate. He did not agree that salvation was by grace alone. Albrecht listened intently to his friends.

"Dr. Eck thinks human inventions have the same authority as the Bible," Lazarus commented dryly.

Kaspar Nutzel, who had translated the *Ninety-Five Theses* into German, added, "The problem is that the Papacy burdens the people with banns and edicts that are not in the Bible."

"Gentlemen," said Willibald in his dramatic voice. "I think we must admit that true Christians sin against their consciences when they submit to the Pope!"

The men grew quiet at this last pronouncement. Albrecht had

finished and sat thinking about Willibald's words.

Willibald noticed Albrecht's illustrations. He hastened to hold the pages up for the others to view. "Albrecht is certainly the most skilled artist I have ever seen," he declared. The somber tone was broken. The men admired each of the illustrations in turn.

"Make one of your jointed people," urged Lazarus.

Albrecht hesitated, but his friends insisted. They watched with fascination as he drew first a body, then legs, arms, and a head, all perfectly proportioned. Willibald produced a pair of scissors and when they were cut out, they fit together perfectly.

"It is like the truth of God's word," said Lazarus. "All the pieces fit together perfectly, though one might not see it at first."

"Your defense of Luther fit together perfectly as well," said Willibald. "Though, of course, I should say that I do not know that it was you who wrote it!"

"It caused quite a stir among Eck and his followers," said Kaspar Nutzel. "It was wise to publish it anonymously. If he could, Dr. Eck would use all his influence to destroy the author of that tract."

"There is another anonymous book that is making a stir," said Lazarus. He watched Willibald as he spoke. "It is called *The Corner*- or as we say in German, *The Eck- Planed Smooth*. It is a hilarious satire against Eck!"

Albrecht noticed that Willibald turned slightly pale at the mention of the book. Could he be the real author? Few men could write satire as he could.

A few weeks later Albrecht was working in his studio when he heard a commotion in the streets. Church bells were ringing though it was not on the hour. Agnes looked up from her accounts. "Hans Baldung, could you find out why the bells are ringing?"

Hans pushed open the heavy oak door and a rush of icy January air stirred the prints that hung on lines.

Hans soon reappeared with the news. "The emperor is dead!" he sputtered. The journeymen and apprentices stopped their work. The work room grew unnaturally quiet.

"He was a good man," said Albrecht. "We served him in life and we will finish the work he left us." As he bade the apprentices to stop work for the day, he exchanged glances with Agnes. He knew she was thinking the same thought he had. What would happen to the pension the emperor had granted him?

As the weeks passed and it became clear that Maximilian's grandson, Charles, would become the next emperor, Albrecht and Agnes laid their plans. The emperor would be crowned in Aachen. They decided to travel to the Netherlands in order to put a petition before the new emperor to extend the pension his grandfather had granted. Agnes worked frantically to make the necessary preparations. The house and workshop would be maintained while they were away.

Albrecht thought they would need a year to travel, make the necessary contacts, and also allow for seeing the sights in the Netherlands. Albrecht sent ahead several boxes of his prints, as well as the prints of Hans Baldung, who was now one of his finest journeymen. He also arranged for Agnes' maid, Susannah, to accompany them.

Albrecht chose the city of Antwerp for their residence. The once sleepy port town was flourishing in its own golden age. The trade with the New World brought exotic products to its ports. The wealth of the city encouraged trade and the arts, and Antwerp was considered the Venice of the north.

A cloud of worry, however, darkened their plans. Shortly before their departure, Willibald burst into the Dürer home.

"Albrecht, I have just received news of the Pope!"

Albrecht noted the extreme pallor of his friend, and led him to a chair. "Is it as we feared? Is Martin Luther in danger of excommunication?"

"It is worse," said Willibald, sinking into the chair. "Lazarus and I have incurred the wrath of the Pope as well!"

Willibald fumbled in his pocket for a piece of paper which he held out for Albrecht to read. It was a copy of an official document of the Pope which named Martin Luther and four other men who would be excommunicated if they did not appear before a council and explain their faith to the satisfaction of the church.

"What does Lazarus say?" asked Albrecht.

"He says it is preposterous. We are citizens of a free city which has always been loyal to the Pope."

Albrecht looked through his window to the gray stones of the Citadel, rising solidly above the town. "I had hoped it would not come to this."

"It is the doing of Eck," said Willibald. "He believes that Lazarus and I were the authors of the anonymous tracts that defended Luther."

Albrecht still stared through the window. "You were, weren't you?" he asked quietly.

Willibald mopped his forehead and looked to make sure that no one else was in the room. "We were, but only a few know that."

"But Eck knows that there are no other men of your caliber who could write such a defense. Lazarus will need all the skills of diplomacy he possesses to fight this battle."

Willibald took his friend by the shoulder. "You will be in the Netherlands. If you can make contact with anyone who can help us, you must! In Belgium look for Erasmus. He is respected for his Greek edition of the Bible. Perhaps he could influence the Pope on our behalf."

"I will do all I can," Albrecht assured him.

Chapter 17

"Much learning is not evil to a man, though some be stiffly set against it, saying that art puffeth up. Were that so, then were none prouder than God who hath formed all arts. But that cannot be, for God is perfect in goodness."
Albrecht Dürer

A Wondrous Journey

The summer sun sparkled on the waters of the Rhine. Albrecht and Agnes stood at the front of the boat and watched the coastline slip away from them. They were on the beginning of a great adventure. Albrecht smiled in anticipation of the new things he might see.

Already they had visited the marvelous "Residenz" of the Bishop of Bamberg, who had given them a travel pass. The pass allowed them to pass without tolls the length of the Main River. The Main brought them to Frankfurt where Albrecht's old client, Jacob Heller, sent them a gift of wine at their inn.

After Frankfurt the Main joined the Rhine, and the Dürers sailed past the green vineyards and beautiful castles lining the river. Some of the castles had the austere bearing of aged grandfathers sitting serenely on the brow of a hill. Other castles bristled with efficiency and importance, and could scarcely allow the boat to pass without extracting an expensive toll. Fortunately Albrecht's travel pass was honored at many of the toll stations.

Agnes had brought her maid, Susannah. Though Agnes had traveled to fairs to sell prints, Susannah had never been outside of Nurnberg. She clutched her travel bag tightly and scarcely spoke as new sights passed before her eyes.

The fifth night the boat reached Cologne. Albrecht's cousin Niklas was a master goldsmith in Cologne. He and his wife greeted the travelers enthusiastically and took them to the Franciscan cloister for a dinner. Albrecht and Niklas eagerly exchanged news of their families. Niklas remembered Albrecht's father with great respect.

"Do you remember how he often said that a work must have a proper foundation?" asked Niklas.

Albrecht nodded. "I have pondered his words over the years, and I believe he meant something deeper than a foundation built on artistic skill."

"I think he was trying to tell me that even in my apprentice days," agreed Niklas. "At first I tried to understand his words by seeking simple designs."

Albrecht laughed. "I did the opposite! I sought beauty in the brightest colors and most complex designs."

"Did you find it?"

"No, it wasn't until after my father died that I realized what he meant by a foundation."

Niklas leaned forward. "What was it?"

"He meant for the foundation to be faith in God. Only then could an artist understand the true beauty as made by the Creator."

Niklas was intrigued by Albrecht's words. Albrecht answered his questions and unfolded the lessons he had been learning in his study of the Bible.

"It is simple," he concluded. "As Martin Luther explained, God gives us eyes to see so that we might believe in Christ and have eternal life. My father's favorite verse from the Bible describes Jesus as the author of eternal salvation. That was the foundation he wanted us to have."

Niklas was quiet for a few moments. "These are perilous times for such thoughts, but I will think long on the things you have said."

Albrecht and Agnes remained in Cologne for five days. Albrecht noticed that his cousin's finances had never recovered after his kidnapping and ransom. Before he left, he quietly gave gifts of money to Niklas' daughters and made a gift of his coat to his cousin.

Albrecht and Agnes arrived in Antwerp on a hazy August evening, two weeks after they had first begun their journey. They were to stay in an inn called the Englenborch which was between the busy harbor and the main market place. The painter's guild already knew of their plans and had arranged a dinner in their honor for the third day after their arrival.

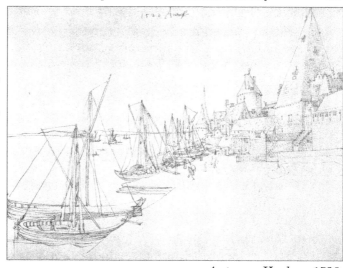

Antwerp Harbor, 1520

The evening of the dinner an escort met the Dürers at the inn and brought them to the guild hall. As they entered, the guild members and their wives stood to greet them and bowed as though they were royalty. They led them to the head of the table, where silver ornaments and serving utensils glimmered in the candlelight. Liveried waiters served costly meats and delicacies.

Albrecht and Agnes enjoyed the delicious food. After the dinner the guild members presented Albrecht with gifts and promised to help him in every way during his stay.

Several town officials were also present. The Syndic of Antwerp presented four cans of wine on behalf of the Town Council. He invited Albrecht to make Antwerp his permanent home and offered him tax-free status, free housing, and an annual salary of three hundred gold Philip's gulden. Albrecht noticed that Agnes' blue eyes grew wide as she heard these offers.

By lantern light the guild officials escorted them home. Albrecht and Agnes agreed that they had never attended a finer dinner in their lives.

The next day the painter's guild invited Albrecht to their warehouse where they were making decorations for the triumphal entry of the emperor. There were four hundred arches that would be set up on both sides of the street. Each arch was forty feet wide and two stories high. The guild master explained that plays would be acted on them.

"How much do they cost?" asked Albrecht.

He was staggered by the answer: four thousand florins! That would feed and house his apprentices for years. Albrecht told Agnes of all the things he had seen. "They spare no expense," he said. "In Antwerp there is enough money for such things."

On a feast day there was a great procession that came past their inn. Albrecht and Agnes watched in amazement as the parade went before them with great pomp and ceremony.

There were pipers and booming drums, costly pole-candles and silver trumpets. All of the guilds marched in order. Each row held signs showing their guild and rank. There were goldsmiths, masons, painters, embroiderers, sculptors, fishermen, butchers, bakers, merchants and many other guilds. As Albrecht wrote to Lazarus and Willibald, "he could never describe it all."

After the religious orders marched, Albrecht thought the parade must be over, but a trumpet announced the arrival of a wagon decorated like a ship. On the ship, men acted scenes from the Bible. The first ship was the Prophet Moses. More ships followed showing other prophets and scenes from the Bible. Then came other stories, such as the Dragon and Saint Margaret. There was even a dashing knight dressed as Saint George. The full procession took two hours.

In the days that followed, Albrecht and Agnes never tired of discussing the new things they were seeing. Albrecht went to Mechelen and Brussels to have his petition drawn up, and saw more amazing and beautiful sights.

He saw a fish bone that was a fathom long and weighed 1,650 pounds, and a great stone that was cast from the sky during a storm. He also saw the elegant Town Hall in Brussels and the Royal Palace with its zoo. He drew pictures of animals and buildings during his short trip.

When Albrecht returned to Antwerp he found Agnes up to her elbows in soapy laundry. She grinned wryly at Albrecht. "It became necessary to purchase our own laundry tub while you were away. Susannah and I decided we could do the laundry much better than these people. And for a much better price, too!"

Albrecht laughed. "*Mein* Agnes, I will have to explain to the launderers' guild why my wife thinks they are not good enough."

Agnes left the laundry with Susannah and eagerly asked about his trip.

"I think it was a success," he began. "Lady Margaret, who is the aunt of our new emperor, sent word that she would speak for me to King Charles."

"And did you see Erasmus as you had hoped?"

Albrecht frowned slightly. "I saw him, but I could not persuade him to defend Luther and our friends. He admits Luther is a godly man, but he will not interfere."

Agnes sniffed in disdain. "I hope the Pope has the commonsense to withdraw the threat of excommunication."

Albrecht went on to tell Agnes of the places and curiosities he had seen. "The most amazing exhibition I saw was a display of art that has recently arrived from the New World, which they call 'the new golden land of Mexico.' It was sent to King Charles from Captain Hernando Cortes."

Susannah had slowed her scrubbing considerably as they talked, and now she stopped altogether and leaned forward to listen.

"There was a sun all made of gold, a fathom wide," said Albrecht drawing his arms wide to illustrate. "And there was a moon all of silver the same size. My father would have loved to have seen the subtle genius of these men in foreign lands. I cannot express all that I thought there."

"Did they have clothes from the golden land?" asked Susannah timidly.

"Yes, there was a whole room of strange clothing and bedspreads decorated with exotic bird feathers. Another room was full of wonderful weapons, armor, darts, and shields. They were more beautiful to me than miracles. All the days of my life I have never seen anything that gladdened my heart so much."

Agnes sighed as he finished his description. "This has been a wondrous journey."

As the summer faded into autumn, Albrecht busied himself with making portraits and selling prints. He still had time to see the triumphal entry of the new emperor and to attend the Coronation as a guest of the Nurnberg delegation.

The Coronation took place in Aachen, the burial place of Charlemagne. While there, Albrecht purchased a Lutheran pamphlet and a pair of eyeglasses. When he brought the eyeglasses home, Agnes liked them so much that he had to buy a second pair for her!

Albrecht also traveled to see his cousin in the autumn. He sketched a picture of Niklas's daughter and once again quietly left gifts for the family. He told Niklas the money for his daughter was simply for *Weckenspitzlein,* a traditional pastry. Of course, the gift would buy much more than that.

Albrecht was saddened to witness a burning of Luther's books and tracts while he was in Cologne.

"Luther sets forth the holy Gospel," he told Niklas. "His books should not be burned!"

Even as Albrecht received the good news that his petition for the pension was granted, he worried how his friends in Nurnberg were faring. Albrecht wrote on a piece of paper:

Therefore all things are in Christ good things. There is nothing good in us except it becomes good in Christ. Whosoever therefore will altogether justify himself is unjust. If we will what is good, Christ wills it in us. No human repentance is enough to equalize deadly sin and be fruitful.

The autumn passed into winter, and Albrecht was the guest in many warm homes. He became good friends with the First Secretary to the Portuguese Consul who gave him marzipan candies and a green parrot for Agnes.

Albrecht visited Erasmus several times. He made his portrait in charcoal and in oil paint. He promised that he would make a woodcut portrait as well. Each time he urged Erasmus, who was famous for his book called *The Manual of a Christian Soldier*, to defend his beleaguered friends. Each time Erasmus said that he could not.

Erasmus of Rotterdam

"We shall all gladly learn, for the more we know so much more do we resemble the likeness of God who verily knoweth all things."
Albrecht Dürer

A Hero

A pounding at the door brought Agnes rushing to open the door. Two men supported Albrecht, one on each side. He was white and shaking with cold, though he wore a second coat.

"What has happened?" Agnes asked anxiously as she directed the men to help her husband to the bed.

The men spoke with the rough accent of sailors. "The captain says he must be helped home. Your husband caught a hot fever on the voyage to Zeeland."

"He was a hero, ma'am and we was grateful," added the second man.

"A hero," Agnes echoed weakly.

"Yes, ma'am, when our ship came to port a bigger ship rammed it. Only the captain, your husband, and a few women were still on board."

"We were sure they were out to sea and would never come back," added the second sailor. "The captain could not bring her round with the storm as it was..."

"The storm?"

"The captain said he gave up, but your husband told him to be brave and think how they could turn the ship. He did the work of five men himself!"

"And saved all the people on board even though he caught a chill," added the second man.

Agnes tried to digest their information, all the while laying more blankets over Albrecht. When the men left, she called Susannah to come quickly. While Susannah went for a doctor, Agnes fed Albrecht some broth. Despite several layers of blankets he continued to shiver violently.

The doctor nodded his head when he saw him. "I have seen this sickness in the winter. You say he went to Zeeland at this time of year?"

Agnes looked grim. "He heard that there was a large whale washed up on the beach there."

The doctor looked at Albrecht with new respect. "I heard of that whale. I would like to have seen it as well. They say it was one hundred fathoms long and three times as big as most whales. It would have taken more than six months to cut and boil it."

"Will they boil it then?" asked Agnes.

"No, I heard that it washed back into the sea in a storm. Your husband was probably too late."

Agnes looked at Albrecht with concern. "His curiosity extracted a heavy price this time."

The doctor gave Agnes medicines and promised to return the next day.

Albrecht slowly recovered. Concerned friends sent medicines and advice. The First Secretary of the Portuguese Consul sent a mixture that he promised could cure any illness. He also sent another parrot.

Several weeks later Albrecht was able to sit in a chair by the fireplace. His face was thinner than usual, and he still wrapped himself in several blankets to keep out the winter chill. He was reading a letter which had arrived from Lazarus Spengler.

"Agnes, did you hear that there was a plague in Nurnberg?"

"The Imhoffs brought the news several months ago. They said that the imperial diet would not be in Nurnberg after all. They would have the diet at Worms instead."

Albrecht nodded. "They had the diet and Lazarus attended. Listen to what he wrote: 'Martin Luther deported himself so courageously, in such a Christian and honorable manner, that I believe that the Romanists and their secret and open supporters would have given thousands of gulden not to have demanded his presence and seen and heard him. Large numbers of nobles as well as common people became his followers upon hearing his testimony. The young emperor impresses me as a sincere young man, but misled by the clergy. The high church officials spent the Holy Week gambling and pursuing worldly trifles! There were two groups there: those who favored the pope rather than divine truth and those who had the good of God's kingdom and the Holy Roman Empire at heart.'"

"To think that the church has come to this!" exclaimed Agnes.

Albrecht waved the letter in the air. "The Papacy puts a heavy load of human laws on people and does not teach the redemption of Christ. These doctrines are invented by men and the precious Word of God is wrongly expounded!"

"We must pray that the church will see the truth soon," said Agnes.

However, the next news that Albrecht received was even worse. Martin Luther had been kidnapped! Albrecht feared for Luther's life. His mind was so troubled he could not eat or sleep. He wrote a long prayer to God in his diary:

...Oh God of heaven pity us! Oh Lord Jesus Christ pray for Thy people! Deliver us at the fit time. Call together Thy far-scattered sheep by Thy voice in the Scripture, called Thy godly Word.... Call together again the sheep of Thy pasture, who are still in part found in the Roman Church, and with them also the Indians, Muscovites, Russians, and Greeks, who have been scattered by the oppression and avarice of the Pope and by false appearance of holiness. Oh God, redeem Thy poor people constrained by heavy bann and edict

...Oh all ye pious Christian men, help me deeply to bewail this man, inspired of God, and to pray Him yet again to send us an enlightened man. Oh Erasmus of Rotterdam, where wilt thou stop? Behold how the wicked tyranny of worldly power, the might of darkness, prevails. Hear, thou knight of Christ! Ride on by the side of the Lord Jesus. Guard the truth.

As Albrecht worried for the progress of the gospel, their time

Agnes Dürer, the artist's wife, in Netherlandish costume.

in Antwerp drew to a close. Though Albrecht and Agnes enjoyed the wonders of the Netherlands, they knew that their home would always be Nurnberg. They longed to return.

Albrecht packed boxes to send ahead of them. He made last-minute portraits for friends. Even as the final plans were made, an urgent message arrived from King Christian of Denmark. He wanted to meet the painter with the hairy beard.

When Albrecht first saw King Christian, he was surprised to learn that he traveled with only two men. The king was a strong individual with an honest face. He looked like a man who did not fear. Nevertheless, Albrecht marveled at the confidence he had to travel through foreign lands without a guard.

Albrecht made a portrait for King Christian. The king liked it so much that he requested a second portrait. Albrecht, eager to return home, completed and framed the portrait in four days. He won the admiration and friendship of the king, who revealed that his faith was the same as Albrecht's own.

At last Albrecht and Agnes began their journey home. As they once again sailed along the Rhine, Albrecht looked through the sketches and water colors he had made during their trip. There were castles, interesting people, and exotic animals like the grumpy walrus who was captured near the Flemish coast.

The last sketch was of Agnes. He had made it on their twenty-sixth wedding anniversary. She wore the Netherlandish headdress he had purchased for her on his trip to Zeeland. Her eyes were the same clear eyes he had sketched so long ago, but they held the wisdom of many years experience, and something more.

Chapter 19

"A fine work of art is well-pleasing to God, and He is angry with such as destroy the works of great mastership, for that is bestowed by God alone."
Albrecht Dürer

Reformation

T he old oaks were beginning to show their spring green. As the snow and ice melted, the Pegnitz River flowed swiftly under the Meat Bridge. The pigeons brought sticks and leaves to their new nests in the steeples of St. Lawrence Church while wagons rolled over the cobbled streets of Nurnberg.

Albrecht hailed one of the wagoneers. The man was dressed in the robe of a monk and he drove a wagon loaded with books. "Sir, what are you doing with a wagon of books?"

"The birds are making their nests and the books are finding a new home as well!" replied the monk with a chuckle.

"Where are you taking them?" asked Albrecht wondering how the monk could make merry over such a topic.

"They are dismantling the convents and monasteries, and all the books will go to make one big library at the old Dominican convent."

"Where is your monastery?"

"It is the old Benedictine monastery. It will be made into the new High School."

Albrecht shook his head in wonder at all the changes. So much had happened since the day he received news of Luther's disappearance. Luther had indeed been excommunicated, but his disappearance was arranged by Elector Frederick of Saxony,

Albrecht's friend and patron. People were beginning to call him "Frederick the Wise." He hid Luther in his castle for ten months to keep him safe.

During that time Luther translated the New Testament from Greek to German. Albrecht thought it was the finest example of German writing he had ever read.

Willibald and Lazarus had been spared excommunication. Willibald's brush with the Pope had made him cautious, but Lazarus' desire to bring the true gospel to Nurnberg had grown even stronger. Lazarus used his considerable skills in diplomacy to bring about a peaceful renewal of the city's churches. He also helped by putting his talents as a poet to good use. He wrote several hymns, which were already being sung in many languages. In time Lazarus Spengler became known as "a jurist among theologians and a theologian amongst jurists."

While some communities roiled with tensions between Catholic and Reformation doctrines, the citizens of Nurnberg peaceably brought the Reformation to their city. Nurnberg churches quietly removed icons or shrouded the church ceilings in their Lenten dust covers.

Many of the priests believed the true gospel. They had been working for years to return the Catholic church to its biblical foundations, but they had come to realize that the Catholic church could not be healed.

The monk interrupted Albrecht's thoughts. "They say that Philip Melanchthon will come to help with the High School."

Albrecht recognized the name of his old friend. "Martin Luther's associate will be in Nurnberg?"

"Yes, and a whole host of others. Some of us will work with them. The Council wants education to have first priority."

Albrecht eagerly took the news to Agnes. "I would like to meet these men when they come," he told her.

Agnes looked up from a receipt book that she was checking. "I'm sure Willibald can arrange it. Though I don't know how you will be able to do all your work and attend more meetings. Willibald does not understand how hard you work."

Albrecht detected a note of impatience in Agnes' voice. "I will try to give more of my work to the assistants. I think this High School is going to be very important."

Agnes sighed and returned to her books. "I only ask that you remember your health when you take on more commitments."

Albrecht saw the growing need for textbooks for artists. Though many ancient books had been re-discovered and translated, instruction by ancient artists such as Apelles were lost. Albrecht threw his energies into completing the textbook that he had been writing for many years. The book grew into several books. The first text was published in 1525 and was called *Measuring with Compass and Rule*. He dedicated the book to Willibald. He hoped that future artists could benefit from the knowledge he had learned. He wrote in the introduction:

Until now we have in this German land of ours set many a clever young lad to learning the art of painting, but we have taught him by rule of thumb without any foundation or reason. Though many have by means of much practice become skillful painters, they are thoughtless fellows, working on impulse alone. Measuring must be the true foundation....

At this time there was confusion among the reformation communities as to what to do with art work that had been used in an idolatrous way. Martin Luther wrote in a tract that "images for memorial and witness such as crucifixes and images of saints" should be tolerated since "they are praiseworthy and honorable as the witness stones of Joshua and of Samuel."

Albrecht gave this topic serious thought. He wrote:

A sword is a sword, which may be used either for murder or justice. Similarly the arts are in themselves good. God has formed that which is good, misuse it how ye will....shun the evil and choose the good; and hereunto serve the arts, for they give the discernment of good and evil. ...For the art of painting is employed in the service of the Church and by it the sufferings of Christ and many other profitable examples are set forth.

One afternoon as Albrecht sat writing at his desk, Willibald arrived for a visit. He enthusiastically told Albrecht that his textbook for artists was selling well. Willibald, with his experience in writing and publishing books, had prepared the manuscript for the publisher and continued to take delight in its progress. As he talked, he noticed the scattered papers on Albrecht's desk. "What are you writing?" he asked.

Albrecht held up a piece of paper that bore an outline with topics including "Forts to be erected principally at the angles of town walls" and "The ideal head-quarters of a king".

"This is a book about the art of fortification."

Willibald raised an eyebrow. "I thought you were going to complete the book on human proportions."

"I am still working on that book, but I have been studying fortifications lately. I thought this book would be useful. I will dedicate it to King Ferdinand of Hungary."

"He could certainly use help in defending against the Ottoman Turks!" replied Willibald, his interest growing despite himself. "If the Ottoman Turks are not stopped in Hungary, they will destroy us all."

Willibald took up one sheet of paper after another and studied each one. One of the chapters was called "How to strengthen the fortification of an old town, no longer strong enough to resist artillery." It could prove useful to the city of Nurnberg. He also saw elaborate schemes for erecting forts, trench defenses, and bomb-proof shelters.

Albrecht gave him a sketch and enthusiastically explained his grandest plan. "If a king wishes to build a defensible castle, he should build a double ring of trenches 50 feet deep and 50 feet broad next to massive walls of masonry 60 feet high and 100 feet broad at the top and 150 feet below."

Willibald shook his head. "Albrecht, your project would be too costly!"

"But consider the Kings of Egypt. They spent vast sums on the pyramids, which are useless, whereas this expenditure would be very useful. If the prince has many poor folk, who otherwise must be supported by alms, let him give them hire for their day's labor. Then they will not dare to beg and will be so much the less ready to riot. It is also better for a prince to spend much money and live in peace, than to be driven forth by his enemy."

Willibald took parts of the draft with him and promised he would study it to see if it would be useful for publication.

Chapter 20

*"Wherefore he that understandeth how to learn somewhat
in his leisure time, whereby he may most certainly be
enabled to honor God and to do what is useful both for
himself and others—that man doeth well; and we know
that in this wise he will gain much experience in art and
will be able to make known its truth for our good."*
Albrecht Dürer

Making Truth Known

The bleak winter light filtered through the bull's eye windows
of the Dürer home. From the window, the towers of the citadel
pierced a leaden sky. "It will snow, I think," Albrecht said as he
sorted through some papers.

Agnes sewed in her chair by the fireplace. "It is a good feeling
to sit by a warm fire when it is cold outside. It is especially cozy
when you know you have a winter's supplies under your roof."

Albrecht neatly tied a bundle of papers together and cut the
cord with a knife. "It seemed a nuisance when the city officials
first required us to stock a half-year's supplies, but now it is a
security not only in case of war, but bad weather, too." Albrecht
stopped suddenly and his eyebrows furrowed in puzzlement.
"Agnes, have you seen the notes on horses that I left here?"

Agnes caught the strained tones in her husband's voice and
hastened to his desk. "I have not seen them for at least a week," she
said slowly. "I thought they were mixed in with all your other papers."

Albrecht called his brother Hans but he knew nothing of the
papers. Albrecht waited several days with the hopes that they
would reappear, but at the end of the week he had to admit that
they were probably stolen. The week before the incident, Albrecht
had dismissed one of his best apprentices when he learned that

the young man had stolen some supplies from the workshop. The youth demonstrated significant ability, but had become involved with a group of Munzerites who met secretly to make plans to overthrow all authority.

When Albrecht found the stolen supplies in the young man's possession, he was heart-broken. He confronted him, but the apprentice defiantly declared that property should be common to all and that he was no more stealing the supplies than Albrecht would be if he used them.

Albrecht was surprised at his brashness. He tried to keep his voice even as he spoke. "Son, no matter what you believe politically, you must obey the Bible. The Judge of heaven must be obeyed and He has declared 'Thou shalt not steal'. Do you understand?"

The young man stared stonily at Albrecht and refused to admit his wrong. Albrecht feared that the young man had added to his guilt by an even greater theft—the theft of his years of research on the proportions of horses.

Later that week Albrecht dined with Willibald and his friends. As usual Willibald arranged for a delicious meal. The men enjoyed pike sprinkled with ginger and bread crumbs, marinated cabbage salad, and raisins and nuts for dessert. When they heard of Albrecht's loss, Willibald heatedly denounced the culprit, but Lazarus was more moderate.

"If the culprit was this young man, you must realize that he has been misled by a powerful idea. Never underestimate the power of an idea to move men, especially young men, to action."

"Are you saying that Albrecht should not pursue the thief?" challenged Willibald. "Albrecht does have rights under the law."

Albrecht stroked his beard. "I had considered that, but I think there is a greater lesson here. I was the boy's teacher and I failed him. I taught him to paint but I was not able to teach him the really important things about God. I have realized that I can still teach him one lesson."

"What lesson could you teach a scoundrel?" asked Willibald.

"I can teach him the lesson of generosity and kindness."

"That is a good choice," said Lazarus. "Our Lord taught us to love our enemies and pray for those who despitefully use you."

"Humph," interjected Willibald. "It seems to me our Lord also promised judgment on those who do evil."

"That is true," replied Lazarus. "But the same Lord who judges, also died on the cross to pay for our sins."

During his final years Albrecht took his responsibility for his apprentices with increasing seriousness. Before he accepted a new apprentice he asked about the boy's home. He tried to learn if the boy had been raised to appreciate truth and beauty. He taught his apprentices that the foundation of all art is Christ.

A summer breeze blew through the open windows of the workshop, and ruffled the fur of a puppy that lay in a pool of sunlight. At a table sat two young boys absorbed in the work of sketching a plump pillow that lay before them.

Albrecht bent over them to inspect their work. He pointed to one of the drawings. "This is good where you have shown the stitches on the pillow. Now you need to shade the pillow so it will look soft and round."

Albrecht studied the second drawing. The apprentice had not only drawn skillfully, but had captured the grain of the fabric, the frayed edges, and even the feeling that the pillow belonged in a home. "Rolf, this is excellent! You have made a work of art from a homely image. That is the secret of great artists."

Rolf blushed with pleasure at the praise. Albrecht left the boys to continue their work while he inspected the progress of his assistants and journeymen.

In one corner stood his newly-completed painting of The Four Preachers. Albrecht looked fondly on the painting which he planned to give to the city of Nurnberg for the city hall. It was his gift to the people of his community. Nearby a calligrapher was painting the text that Albrecht wanted to be attached to the painting. He had written:

All worldly rulers in these dangerous times should give good heed that they receive not human misguidance for the Word of God, for God will have nothing added to His Word nor taken away from it. Hear therefore these four excellent men, Peter, John, Paul, and Mark, their warning.

Underneath each of the men would be a Bible verse taken from Luther's German translation of the Bible. Albrecht wanted everyone to be able to read and understand what the four men said in the Bible. While Albrecht studied the painting, Agnes slipped up behind him.

"You will miss the four preachers when they are moved to the City Hall?" she asked.

"I will miss them, but that is where they belong."

While Agnes called the apprentices and journeymen for the noon-day meal, Albrecht lingered in the workshop. There was still so much he wanted to do. The final proofs of the text on fortifications were ready, and the textbook on human proportions was nearing completion.

His greatest work, however, would be a textbook for artists. It was the culmination of notes that he had been preparing for over twenty years. He thought he would call it "Teaching in Painting" or "Food for Young Artists."

A loose piece of paper caught his eye. It was a note he had written several years ago. Albrecht read again the words that continued to guide his life:

Seeing that through disobedience of sin we have fallen into everlasting Death, no help could have reached us save through the incarnation of the Son of God, whereby He through His innocent suffering might abundantly pay thee Father all our guilt, so that the Justice of God might be satisfied. For he has repented of and made atonement for the sins of the whole world, and has obtained of the Father Everlasting Life. Therefore Christ Jesus is the Son of God, the highest power, who can do all things, and He is the Eternal Life. Into whomsoever Christ comes he lives, and himself lives in Christ.

Albrecht placed the paper on top of his notes. When he considered the art he had pursued during his life, he felt a satisfaction that he had shown these truths in all his work. With a last glance at the Four Preachers, he went to join the others for the meal.

Four Preachers

Knight, Death, and the Devil, 1513

"A well-instructed and experienced artist may show more power and insight in a rustic image of small size than another in his great work"

Albrecht Dürer

Epilogue

A lbrecht Dürer was counted among the leading intellectuals of the early sixteenth century. As an artist he made the acquaintance of men like Emperor Maximilian, Emperor Charles V, Erasmus, Melanchthon and Martin Luther. He was one of the first German artists to rise above the status of "craftsman," becoming the renaissance idea of a scholar. He was also the first German artist to write about artistic theory. The Christian worldview which he brought to the field of art is still relevent today. When he died on April 6, 1528, he left more than seventy paintings, over one hundred engravings, two hundred and fifty woodcuts, more than a thousand drawings, and several books.

Erasmus called Dürer "the Apelles of his day." He claimed that Dürer could show more in black and white than could Apelles with all his colors. He elevated the medium of printmaking to a fine art.

A contemporary of Dürer contrasted him to artists who "sought vulgar celebrity by immodest pictures". He wrote: "Albrecht, therefore, shall we most justly admire as an earnest guardian of piety and modesty." He also wrote: "All these perfections he attained by reducing mere practice to art and method, in a way new at least to German painters.... He had brought painting into the fixed track of rule and recalled it to scientific principles... He first worked his principle out for his own use; afterwards with his generous and open nature he attempted to explain them in books." Albrecht's generosity was also reflected in the scholarship fund which his wife Agnes endowed to enable sons of craftsmen to study liberal arts and theology.

Dürer was an eyewitness and participant in the Reformation. He helped to bring the Bible to a wide audience through his brilliant illustrations of the book of Revelation and other themes. His woodcuts were meant to be affordable for ordinary people. His *Apocalypse* was printed along with the complete Bible passage. Dürer wanted to show the supremacy of the Bible while using his art to preach sermons to those who could not read. His diaries and notes reflect his sincere and vibrant Christian faith. Melanchthon said that "though Dürer excelled in the art of painting, it was the least of his accomplishments."

We can learn about Albrecht Dürer's life from the letters, diaries, and works of art which he left to history. Many people do not know that the popular "Praying Hands" sketch was made by Albrecht Dürer. The sketch was a study for an altarpiece that he painted. Some historians believe the hands were his mother's.

At Dürer's death Martin Luther wrote, "It is natural and right to weep for so excellent a man."

Illustrations

Bibliography and Sources of Art Work by Dürer

Braham, Allan, _Dürer_, London: Spring Books, 1965

Conway, William Martin, _The Writings of Albrecht Dürer_, New York: Philosophical Library, Inc., 1958

Fry, Roger, _Dürer's Record of Journeys to Venice and the Low Countries_, New York: Dover Publications, Inc., 1995

Hutchison, Jane Campbell, _Albrecht Dürer: A Biography_, Princeton: Princeton University Press, 1990

Kurth, Willi, ed., _The Complete Woodcuts of Albrecht Dürer_, New York: Dover Publications, Inc., 1963

Kusch, Eugen, _The Immortal Nurnberg_, Nurnberg: Hans Carl, 1972

Monneret, Simon, _Dürer_, New York: Excalibur Books,1979

Russell, Francis, _The World of Dürer: 1471-1528_, New York: Time Incorporated, 1967

Wolfflin, Heinrich, ed., _Drawings of Albrecht Dürer_, New York: Dover Publications, Inc., 1970

Books for Young Readers:

Caselli, Giovanni, _A German Printer_, New York: Peter Bedrick Books, 1986

Raboff, Ernest, _Albrecht Dürer: Art for Children_, New York: Harper and Row, 1988

Acknowledgments

With special acknowledgment to Dover Publishing for their kind permission to print artwork from *The Complete Woodcuts of Albrecth Dürer,*, *The Complete Engravings, Etchings & Drypoints of Albrecht Dürer* and *The Drawings of Albrecht Dürer.*

The author wishes to express her gratitude to the staff of Greenleaf Press for their time and skill in proofreading, and the librarians of Largo Library for their help in research.

The quotations from Dürer's writings were translated by W.M. Conway in *Literary Remains of Albrecht Dürer*, Cambridge University Press, 1889. Poems were translated by Mrs. Charles Heaton in *Life of Albrecht Dürer.*

Made in the USA
Monee, IL
23 April 2023

32312146R00069